The Body Language of Illness

The Body Language of Illness

By Eleanor Limmer, ACSW, MSW

Cover Art:
Lynn Guier
Spirit Lake, Idaho

Published by:
Freedom Press
1227 S. Liberty Drive
Liberty Lake, WA 99019

Printed in the United States of America

0-9678183-1-1

Preface

The Philosophy of The Body Language of Illness

The philosophy behind this book is a holistic one that looks at wellness as a continuum. Wellness is not merely the absence of illness or physical symptoms. Each of the mental, emotional, physical and spiritual parts of ourselves are interwoven and affect our health and happiness. To be well, a person needs to continually search and stretch to reach his or her unique wholeness. Once this wholeness is found, life becomes less stressful and self-regulation allows us to master our body and our health. This book is based on the principle that a physical illness is symbolic of a mental, emotional or spiritual conflict that can be discovered and healed.

The holistic philosophy of this book comes from my belief that everything that happens to us in life carries meaning if we allow ourselves to listen to it. Every bodily symptom from a scratch on the knee to a cancerous tumor carries a message we can listen to and answer. If we listen to the whispers of the small cuts and bruises of our lives, we will not have to hear the loud shouts of a major illness such as cancer or a heart attack.

This holistic view of illness is an empowering one. It helps us see that we create the conflict that is symbolized by illness, and that there are always ways to resolve this conflict.

The dark, suffering side of illness can prove to be the challenge that awakens us to a broader perspective of a more peaceful, healthier way of life. This approach to illness is an intuitive, intellectual one that explores the individual's experience to determine what a particular symptom symbolizes. At the same time, this holistic approach recognizes that there are patterns or archetypes of the body which serve as clues that can help us read the messages of illness.

This holistic approach to illness is more inclusive than approaches that depend upon intellect or the physical alone. This approach takes into consideration all parts of our experience—our thoughts as well as our feelings, and inner wisdom and intuition as well as intellect. Traditionally, the symptoms of an illness are the primary focus of attention. This holistic philosophy views the emotional, mental and spiritual conflicts underlying these symptoms as more important. Once these conflicts are resolved, the body knows how to heal itself automatically. This book is about how you can listen to, understand and answer the messages of illness.

Acknowledgements

I acknowledge with many thanks those who helped me with this book. I especially thank Aaron Smith for his proof reading and editing of my manuscript. I also wish to express my gratitude to those whose stories are included in this book. Although names and other personal information, not related to an illness, have been changed or omitted in respect for privacy, all of the stories included in this book are true. These life stories have helped me to better understand the body language of illness. It was a privilege to share with these individuals the joys and sorrows of their healings, which have been a catalyst for my own healing. I appreciate the strength and courage that allowed these people to seek the good health they desired. Special thanks also goes to my family–Donald, Leah, and Eric–whose loving support helped me to persist in this writing project.

Contents

Chapter One

The Messages of Illness

There is a symbolic body language of illness that uses the activities, functions and parts of the body to express emotional, mental or spiritual conflicts. Each of us can learn to understand and respond to this language to heal ourselves. Healing an illness involves the intuitive-intellectual process of asking how what is happening in our bodies is symbolic of what is happening in our emotional, mental and spiritual lives.

Every illness has a hidden meaning. Healing an illness involves asking what that meaning is, deciphering the symbolic messages of the body, then responding to these messages by making the changes that are indicated. An illness is a symbolic message from your body to get your attention concerning some important conflict, some state of emotional, mental or spiritual imbalance that needs to be faced. Your body gives its messages in specific areas corresponding to your inner conflicts for a number of reasons. The symbols of the body are the purest form of language; they bypass your conscious censoring. You may not consciously wish to face what is unbalanced in your life; therefore you might resist that knowledge.

In the honesty of the symbolic language of the body, it is possible to face the mental-emotional-spiritual conflict beneath your physical symptoms that is vital to your growth and health.

While the negative part of yourself–the negative ego that denies and resists any responsibility for an illness–makes understanding more difficult, you can intuitively understand the symbolic message by asking what is happening specifically to your body and how that corresponds to your emotional, mental and spiritual life. For instance, if you have had a heart attack, you can ask, "How does an attack or dysfunction of my heart relate to my defense against expressing nurturing and loving feelings, to myself and others?"

Responses to the Body Language of Illness

One of the greatest blockages to healing an illness is to look for its cause with the intellect alone. When this is not successful, the feeling of suffering unfairly that follows blocks the healing that could otherwise take place. Healing comes through the realization that every illness carries a message, and that you can understand that message through an intuitive intellectual process. When you learn how to read the symbolic clues of this language, these clues will suggest what needs to be healed beyond the body. Heart disease, for example, suggests the need to express more love, especially self-love.

When faced with an illness or a bodily pain or symptom, you have three basic choices for the attitude you adopt. The *first choice* is the traditional, most common one in our world. This choice denies that this symptom or illness has any meaning to you. When you make this choice, you deny your power and open yourself to attitudes of self-pity and blame.

The *second choice* is to see an illness as a purely one-dimensional physical phenomena caused by genetics or environment. While making changes in your physical life such as in the areas of nutrition, exercise and life-style are helpful and may allow you to live longer, these changes still may not heal the core issues of a symptom or illness. This choice does not deal with how you created this particular illness, at this particular time.

2

The *third choice* is a holistic one in which you choose to examine your specific symptom or illness as symbolic of conflicts in your mental, emotional and spiritual life. This choice empowers you through using the intuitive, emotional knowledge we all possess, but often block. If, for instance, you are "stiff-necked" and have a pain in your neck, it would be wise not only to treat your physical symptom, but to look at how you can be less rigid and inflexible in your attitudes.

One of the most obvious symbolic messages relates to the bodily symbolism that underlies stomach problems such as ulcers and indigestion. When you are unable to process some situation, a common expression or cliche you might use is, "I cannot stomach that." You mean that you refuse to process, handle and let go of some situation. Instead of coping with it, you brood over it and it sticks in your gut, where you carry it around until your stomach bleeds or refuses to function properly. The main function of an illness is to restore balance by calling attention to a mental, emotional or spiritual conflict.

The process of finding the message of an illness requires no special psychic powers, only a willingness to perceive intuitively the deeper symbolic meaning inherent in illness. This process assumes that we all create our illnesses and that we can recreate our health by honestly considering the conflicts that underlie our bodily symptoms.

Mark, a neighbor, recently began looking like a concentration camp resident. He grew thinner daily, and then his stomach closed entirely. An emergency operation was required to open and remove part of his closed intestinal tract. While he was in the hospital recovering, he began exploring the underlying meaning of his painful illness. Mark was careful about his diet and did not abuse alcohol, but he did have something that "he could not stomach." He felt his boss had berated and cheated him. Mark came to the intuitive awareness that it was his anger at his boss that had caused his stomach problem. Mark's anger at the abusive behavior of his boss had settled in his stomach, and while his co-workers left, Mark paid the price of a painful, nearly fatal illness.

If you do not understand the underlying message of an illness, you cannot conceive of the necessity of creating a new way of life to replace it. Understanding the message of an illness is important, because it helps you begin to shift your perspective and imagine a new way of life. The Type A person who suffers from heart disease, for instance, often believes that life is a struggle–all action and will. This person can begin to imagine what it would be like to live creatively, without struggle, and to give him- or herself the freedom to enjoy life. In my practice as a counselor using Guided Imagery and Music for healing, I help people to understand the messages of illness and to answer them by conceiving new life patterns.

Our bodies tell us of imbalances by affecting the areas that most correspond in function to our deeper conflicts. I counseled a young woman named Mary who was suffering from arthritis in her knees. When we explored the message of this illness together, it became obvious to us that Mary was stuck in a life situation which was very stagnant and stifling for her, but that she would not leave because she feared she could not get anything better. Mary had a dream in which she was sitting at work with a blanket over her head. When we discussed this dream, Mary realized that it was telling her that in her work she felt faceless, lacking all identity. Her body was telling her that she was being inflexible, unbending, allowing her negative ego to run her life rather than loving and respecting herself.

The messages of illness are always preceded by subtler, more gentle messages in the form of dreams and intuitions that we have refused to acknowledge. An illness always represents some communication from our bodies that symbolizes an inner emotional or mental conflict that we have previously ignored. Anyone who suffers from a major illness has been warned in numerous ways before the illness began. This communication process is like that of a friend who wants to reach you. This friend sends letters, calls on the phone, but receives no response. If your friend knows you must be home, he may then pay you a visit and knock on your door. When you still will not respond, your friend might get concerned and might try to get in your house by breaking a window or knocking down a door. An illness can be compared to this violence. Since you will not pay attention to some important issue in your life, that issue is expressed symbolically through the body language of illness.

The Challenge of an Illness

Each illness challenges us to come to a new awareness. If we have been tuned into the messages our bodies have been giving us, through our dreams, life experiences, intuitions and inner guidance, an illness will not be necessary. An illness is never a punishment from either our higher selves or God. We create our own illnesses; they represent choices we made which caused inner conflicts and which are given symbolic expression through specific bodily symptoms. Illnesses such as heart defects or physical disabilities serve as a challenge to help us grow in some important way. There may be better ways to learn than through suffering and illness, but if we refuse to learn in these better ways, we sometimes force the more difficult road.

An illness or accident is a warning signal to tell us to watch out, slow down, stop or proceed with caution. An illness is always a way to attract our attention, to suggest that we make some changes in our inner and outer realities. Facing an illness as a message that can be answered, we can prevent further illness through healing our present imbalances and conflicts, and preventing other similar symptoms.

In becoming a poet, I realized that everything that happened to me was meaningful and related to nature, but as a holistic counselor I was more skeptical. I intuitively knew there was a symbolic meaning behind every illness, but I did not completely believe this until it was demonstrated again and again in the lives of the people I worked with. Our entire reality is constantly sending us messages; part of that reality is our physical bodies. The more quickly we listen to the whispers of our lives, the more quickly we can answer them so they do not have to shout at us with illness and pain.

This means we need to pay attention to and trust in our bodies, intellects, intuition, feelings and inner guidance. The body is a powerful source of information to us. The body has a consciousness of its own that is connected with the mind, but different from it. We can best communicate with the consciousness of our bodies through our subconscious minds in a relaxed state of body and mind. It is possible to communicate with the body directly in a relaxed, intuitive way, providing an awareness of the problems underlying a bodily symptom.

While counseling Bob in a Guided Imagery and Music session, I asked about the afflicted parts of his body to determine what was causing them to hurt. Bob had recently left a job that he had held for 22 years and was going through conflict over this change in his life. Meanwhile, his right knee hurt so much he could not walk up or down stairs without considerable pain. His right elbow and thumb also ached. When we addressed the trouble in his right knee, asking, "What is the problem there?" the answer was, "I am afraid I will be unable to put my best foot forward." The pain in his right elbow and thumb pertained to feelings of anger he felt toward the management, whom he felt had treated him and his fellow employees callously. After Bob recognized and faced his fears and anger, the pain disappeared.

Refusing to answer the message of an illness is saying, "No one is at home, no one will respond, no one who loves himself or herself will answer." To be able to respond you must go over to the phone or door and say, "Hello." The things that can keep us from responding include fear of the unknown, inertia, projection upon life or others, or identification as a victim, martyr or hurt child. The choice of whether or not to respond to the message of an illness is critical in many cases. For if the challenge of an illness is not answered, it may come again and again with even more pain and suffering, until the hidden message of the illness is answered.

Barry Neil Kaufman, in his fictionalized autobiography, *A Sense of Warning*, tells how his career and family life were disintegrating because of his chronic migraine headaches. After these headaches became so severe that he could not see, and no medical doctor had been able to help him, he turned to a teacher named Luke for help. Luke taught Kaufman that his migraine headaches were a friend and teacher and not to resist them. These headaches disappeared when Kaufman began trusting his own inner wisdom and intuitions. When they did reappear in times of great stress, instead of resisting them, Kaufman learned to let go and become aware of himself separate from the pain. By following his intuitions, dreams and inner guidance, Kaufman was able to not only get rid of his migraine headaches, but also to prevent an impending disaster that might have caused the death of his baby daughter Rachel.

Good Health as a Continuum

To understand illness, it is necessary to understand that health is more than just the absence of physical symptoms or illnesses. Health is a optimal state of emotional, mental and spiritual well being. Since health is a dynamic state that is ever growing and in motion, most of us still have areas of weakness or illness that could in time manifest as physical symptoms if we do not heal them.

Lazaris defines health as containing several components. The first one is a search for your life's purpose with an aliveness that is filled with the vibrancy of love, trust, enthusiasm and expectancy. It is the process of seeking and finding the four powers of life: freedom, action, giving and joy. These powers give us the ability to act and to be filled with their essence.

Good health is living your life with an elegance and grace in which you get the greatest result from the least amount of energy. Your life flows with grace, dignity and style rather than stumbling over conflict and struggle. Elegance comes from clarifying your desire and stepping into your possibilities rather than struggling with your environment. Finally, good health is the wellness that comes with trusting yourself and those worthy of trust. It is being spiritually connected through the vibrancy of loving and co-creating your life with enthusiasm and joy.

Illness is a symbol of disorientation, alienation, disorder or failure. An illness of *disorientation* occurs when you are out of touch with your emotions and are no longer searching for your life's focus or purpose, or when you fail to communicate and express your unique Self. An illness of *alienation* occurs when you feel cut off from your spirituality–your sense of unity with the world, nature, other people, the universe, and your God. An illness of *disorder* manifests itself when your life has lost a sense of understanding and meaning, and you have no method of seeking or expressing your spirituality. People with heart disease, for example, are usually those who do not follow the impulses of their heart. Often these people are overachievers, motivated by fear to prove themselves, or by beliefs which do not take into consideration the needs of the emotions–the heart.

Your belief system has failed if you are ill, not through moral fault, but from a lack of trust, love, expectancy and enthusiasm. Success seems to be out of reach or impossible for you because of your own lack of internal values, such as self-esteem, integrity, depth of feeling and honesty. No matter how successful you are in the material world, if your life lacks aliveness, depth and meaning, *failure* is present if you have failed to realize the sense of emotional satisfaction that comes with truly appreciating and enjoying your life.

Anything that helps you have less disorientation, disorder, alienation and failure in your life contributes to your health. Any activity, such as oil painting or playing the piano, that brings you joy contributes to your health. You have not failed if you become ill, but the belief system that caused you to be ill certainly has; it created the kind of life style that *created* your illness.

The awareness of how you created an illness can be a source of great inspiration. By seeing how you create an illness, you can then identify those beliefs that need to be changed, and you can release and express those emotions that have been held in the body.

One dramatic example of the kind of freedom that comes with responsibility and insight was that of a woman named Denise who had been diagnosed as having the early stages of Hodgkin's disease. Denise came to The Spokane Healing Arts Clinic, where I helped her search for an alternative regimen of healing and made a holistic assessment of how she had created her illness.

When Denise was asked how her physical condition was symbolic of her emotional, mental and spiritual life, she saw a direct correspondence. Her immune system was dysfunctional and seemed to have lost its will, and her blood was gradually losing its normal blood cells; correspondingly, Denise had lost her own will to live–becoming a martyr to all those around her, especially her husband. She felt that if people really knew who she was, she would be unloved. Since she had become a wife and mother, her sense of alienation from her own powers and life focuses had gotten even worse.

Although Denise was suffering from a life-threatening illness, that illness was really only the symptom of the actual underlying problem: imbalance in the form of disorientation, alienation and lack of vitality. Denise was disoriented from living out a persona, and not allowing herself to be real or to seek her own purposes and focuses in life. She experienced alienation, especially from her own powers, because she gave up her power to other people. Denise believed that if she allowed people to know her, they would reject and abandon her. Denise felt little sense of her own power, enthusiasm or aliveness because she trusted others rather than herself. Her conception of God was of one who rewarded sufferers and saints, and Denise felt that deep down she was a sinful person.

However, Denise had a deep honesty, and part of her welcomed her illness in the face of her despair over her life. By seeing how she had created her illness, Denise could also see the ideals and attitudes that needed to replace those that had been destructive to her. Denise went away from our clinic with renewed hope and courage, and with a plan to heal herself and open up to others.

Illness is often the result of refusing to face the truth about our lives, although this truth has been in us and around us for a long time. Janice had lived with a perfectionist, alcoholic husband for years. It was not until she was in the hospital for a cancer operation that she began to face her true feelings about her life with her husband. One of the nurses began talking to Janice about her feelings and thoughts associated with cancer. This nurse suggested that cancer often was related to suppressed feelings, and that Janice might explore the inner causes of her cancer.

When Janice began this exploration, she knew intuitively that the cancer had to do with suppressed anger she felt at living with an alcoholic husband who constantly projected his anger and guilt upon her. Janice made the decision to leave her husband and begin a new life for herself shortly after leaving the hospital. She had stayed so long with this man because of her own ideas about what a good wife and mother should be. Meanwhile, she had devalued, denied and ignored her suppressed anger. This anger finally expressed itself as cancer.

Janice believed she should martyr herself to maintain a marital relationship. Although her marriage was demeaning to her, she thought of herself as the noble center of the family, until her children told her how they, too, had suffered. Janice had to face her tendency to be a long-suffering martyr who suppressed and invalidated her feelings before she could recover fully from her cancer. When Janice took responsibility for her cancer, instead of feeling guilty, she felt empowered. She knew if she had the power to create her illness, she could also recreate her life with a new sense of power, joy and vitality.

Responsibility and Illness

We are responsible for our health, but this does not mean we should blame ourselves and waste time feeling guilty for an illness. When we recognize how we have created an illness, we then have to own it or take responsibility for it, and then forgive ourselves for this miscreation. The physical symptoms of an   illness are symbolic keys that can open the door to the larger meaning of it. I once counseled a woman who had cancer of the colon. Much of our work together was in exploring ways in which she repressed her feelings. Her healing consisted of expressing all the anger and resentments against her sister and family that she had been holding onto for years.

The need to take responsibility for your own illness should in no way interfere with your using all helpful medical treatment available for an illness, including alternative and traditional ways of healing. Nor should taking responsibility for creating an illness lead you away from a fully cooperative relationship with your doctor. No matter what doctors may tell us, the final responsibility for whether we live, die or get well is ours. It is not a matter of whether or not we are responsible for an illness. We are responsible for creating our illnesses, just as we are responsible for everything else in our lives–including good health. The real issue is when we will assume this responsibility. Illness represents responsibility postponed–where the responsibility for some inner conflict has not been resolved on a mental-emotional-spiritual level, so it is expressed on a physical one.

A major illness such as cancer, arthritis or heart disease can be seen as one big responsibility that is expressed physically because an individual has postponed taking responsibility for the destructive conflicts it represents on some other level. One of the reasons people do not wish to take responsibility for the creation of an illness is they think they will then have to blame themselves for it, and thus add the misery of blame to the suffering from their illness. Taking responsibility for an illness need not involve blame, although we live in a world which likes to blame. If you were not responsible for an illness, you could have no power to re-create your health. Responsibility is an opportunity; not a burden.

You can come to the realization that although blame is common in our world, it is dangerous to our health. Blame can not only make you ill, it can kill you; it affects your heart. Accepting responsibility for an illness does not mean that we ignore factors such as diet, smoking or environmental pollutants which may aggravate it, but that we recognize those factors only lower our resistance to it. Many people exposed to the same influences do not become ill. Eighty percent of heavy smokers, for instance, never acquire lung cancer or emphysema.

If you have to blame someone for your illness, blame yourself; but accelerate this process by doing it intensely, so your discomfort with it will cause you to let it go. It is important to understand that blame in any of its ugly forms (towards yourself, others, God, life, your parents, etc.) has never done anyone any good. Blaming others or life is much more comfortable than blaming yourself. If you blame yourself with intensity, you will soon become so uncomfortable, you may just have to stop criticizing and judging yourself. Silent blame of others or self-blame helps no one. Blame in any of its manifestations has never offered a solution nor made an illness better. We are not talking about blaming criminals here, but about the processing of an illness. Ask yourself whether blame ever made an illness go away or made it better. Did blame allow a tumor to vanish? Does blaming God or life for your illness in any way improve your health or spiritual life?

When illness occurs, it is dishonest to say it is the best thing for you; it brings much suffering and great unhappiness. Illness may be the only way to get your attention at the time, and good can come of it, but you can learn better ways to grow. Illness can be a challenge demanding changes in consciousness that somehow you were not able to make in a happier and wiser way. If we cannot grow through joy, sometimes we are forced to grow through suffering. Often such changes are made under difficult circumstances when you are ill. If you are ill, instead of succumbing to despair, it is important to use the illness to evaluate where in your life there is a conflict that has lead to disorientation, failure and alienation.

Literary Comments on Illness as
Symbolic Metaphor

I have found in my experience as a holistic health counselor that every illness is symbolic of an important conflict. I believe as Bernie Siegel and other holistic doctors and counselors do that viewing an illness as a symbol or metaphor is an opportunity to understand and heal it. If you look at what the specific symbols of a disease mean to you, you can find and change the pattern that created it.

In *Illness as Metaphor*, Susan Sontag argues that giving illness meaning by seeing it as a metaphor with larger meaning invariably leads to a moralistic position that places blame upon the ill. I disagree with Sontag for a number of reasons. First, her position denies the experience of generations of literary artists who have written about their intuitive insights concerning their own illnesses and those of others. Secondly, I disagree with the position that giving meaning to an illness automatically leads to self-blame and self-punishment. To blame oneself is to place a negative judgement upon oneself that causes hurt and does no one any good. Understanding is not the same as laying blame.

Such prominent writers as Keats, Tolstoy, Thomas Mann, Mansfield, Auden, and Kafka recognized that illness does have a metaphorical meaning that surpasses the limitations of logical, linear thought. By denying the insights of these literary artists and seeing tuberculosis as a simple matter of bacilli that can be treated by drugs, Sontag has limited herself to linear thought alone. We can learn much from the insights of these writers who used their deep knowing to produce art which has inspired us with its truth.

Lawrence LeShan is a researcher who purposefully reads what poets and writers have said about an illness to see if he is on the right track before he begins his research. LeShan is aware that writers and poets often tap into truths before scientists do, especially concerning the darker side of life that includes illness, because they depend upon the inspiration from their subconscious minds.

13

Many of the classics of literature have been about illness and death and how they change people's lives. In *The Death of Ivan Ilyich* by Tolstoy, Ivan is dying of cancer, and will not reveal it to his family. The calamity of his disease is symbolic of an entire life of self-deception and a failure of character. When he is dying, he is for the first time in a state of truth, being truly honest with himself. Illness can be seen as a form of self-expression that represents something going on within, that the person involved does not entirely recognize or wish to change. Kafka, after his tuberculosis was diagnosed in September, 1917, wrote in his diary, "...the infection in your lungs is only a symbol, the symbol of an emotional wound whose inflammation is called F(elice)." Disease is an expression of the inner self, but without the moralistic nor punitive connotations many people have placed upon it.

During the last century, tuberculosis was a common disease, particularly among writers, artists and sensitive people who had great feeling, love and passion, but who often suppressed it. Many of these creative people communicated with their subconscious minds and inner inspiration and had insight into the origin of their illnesses. The poet Keats associated his separation from his lover Fanny Brown with his tuberculosis.

The suppression of love and creative enthusiasm can be as destructive as the suppression of anger or fear. In tuberculosis, the ability to breathe is suppressed as the lungs die away, and the patient is consumed by his or her emotions. There is not enough insight. The lungs die away because the passionate person will not allow himself to act upon or express the inner passion that is consuming his life. The sick individual is consumed physically and emotionally by her unexpressed feelings. Literary expression may be the only outlet in which this emotion finds expression. Shelly wrote to Keats, consoling him in his illness by saying, "Consumption is a disease particularly fond of people who write good verse as you have done." (Sontag, 1977)

Tuberculosis is a disease of extreme contrasts, causing a white pallor and red flush, hyperactivity alternating with fatigue. It is a disease of liquids where the respiratory system is filled with phlegm, mucous and finally blood. Above all, there is a need for air. This physical condition symbolizes an inner imbalance where there is too much emotion (the fluids) and too little understanding (the air). The individual is consumed by self-pity and despair, leading to illness.

Kafka's letters offer a wealth of speculation about the meaning of tuberculosis in his life. Kafka thought of his illness as a symbol of his inner conflict over love. He wrote to Max Brod, "The illness is speaking for me because I have asked it to do so, and to Felice. Secretly, I don't believe this illness to be tuberculosis, at least not primarily tuberculosis, but rather a sign of my general bankruptcy." (Sontag, 1977)

The discovery of strong antibiotics has made the "rest cures" of the past obsolete and tuberculosis need no longer be life-threatening. This does not change the message tuberculosis brings to sick people–there is an imbalance in their emotional life, a suppression of feelings that threatens to "consume" or drown them.

Modern Medicine Discovers the Symbolism of Illness

Bernie Siegel, cancer surgeon and author of *Love, Medicine and Miracles*, wrote about his experiences with cancer patients who survived their illnesses through courage and love. It was his observation that the location in which cancer occurred in the body was not just accidental, but usually carried meaning symbolic of the underlying conflicts causing the disease. Siegel called the areas of the body that symbolized the location of an inner emotional, mental or spiritual conflict "target areas."

Over the years, Siegel has observed numerous examples of how the location of a cancer has specific meaning. One such patient was a psychologist named Lee with carcinoma of the larynx. Since Lee was a nonsmoker, this was an unusual location for his tumor. Lee knew intuitively that there were psychological factors involved in his illness and he traced these to his early childhood programming. Often when Lee was a boy and would talk loudly, his father would put his hand around his throat and squeeze it, telling him, "Shut up, Lee, shut up!" in a husky, whispery voice remarkably similar to the sound of Lee's own after the appearance of the cancerous tumor. With some work, Lee released the childhood programming that told him to stifle his self expression in his throat. Despite a grim prognosis, Lee recovered completely. (Siegel, 1986, p. 88.)

In his practice as a cancer surgeon, Dr. Siegel has seen much evidence to support the idea that the location of cancer symbolizes its underlying conflict. Many of his patients already intuitively know what this symbolic connection is. One patient told Siegel, "I was always considered spineless, and here I've developed multiple myeloma of my backbone." (Siegel, 1986) Siegel believes that we sensitize the target organ of our bodies that symbolizes our inner conflict in the form of "negative biofeedback." One multiple sclerosis patient, whose household help left her with five young children to care for, lost the use of her right hand. Immediately before her right hand became immobile, she had lost her right-hand helper. (Siegel, 1986) Another way to understand the specific symbolism of an illness is to think of it as an indication of conflict or dysfunction. Merely removing cancer of the uterus surgically, without healing the imbalance it represents, does not heal the conflict which caused it, and which may strike again.

Toward a Holistic Language of Illness

The symbolic language of an illness allows an ill person to see an illness as a process he or she has created. The true feelings we have concerning a conflict that is expressed in illness are often denied or repressed. One way to bring these feelings to consciousness is through Guided Imagery and Music. I once counseled a women named Jennifer who was scheduled to have surgery for cancer of the cervix. Jennifer denied the existence of any emotional issues underlying her illness, but with the tools of imagery and music she allowed all the rage and sorrow she felt for her ex-lover to emerge. Jennifer was able to confront the image of her lover and tell him of her anger, sorrow and unrequited love.

The principle of correspondence–that what is happening in the body corresponds in likeness or similarity to what is happening in the life of the individual–is why a women who is angry about a past sexual relationship might get cancer in her sexual organs, or someone who doesn't want to hear certain things may develop a hearing problem. Andrea, for instance, came to me to explore the meaning behind her "otis sclerosis," a hardening of the inner membrane of the ear that leads to deafness, which medical science says is incurable. It was clear to Andrea as we explored the meaning of her illness that the ringing in her ears was like an alarm going off in her head, and that she had hardened herself and stopped trusting what she heard and felt in an effort to perfectly gain the love and approval of a difficult boss and her husband. When Andrea began trusting herself and responding to her own inner knowledge and to her senses, her hearing improved.

The language we use to describe and treat an illness is important because it defines how we see an illness. It is most desirable to use the symbolic language of an illness that already exists if we can learn to recognize and use it. We use expressions such as, "It is breaking my back," or "He has hardened his heart," without recognizing how these attitudes lead to back problems and heart disease. It is as though an illness were an unfortunate accident, sad fate or destiny over which we have no responsibility or control.

An illness can be seen as a process in which the body is trying to adapt, to bring the body into balance to compensate for an inner state of conflict or disequilibrium. This soma conflict directly expresses the psyche conflict. "It is not possible in biology to set up a partition between mind and body," observed Henry Maudaley, a distinguished English psychiatrist. "Mind does not merely affect the body, it permeates its constitution...there is not a function of any organ of the body which does not enter into the constitution of the mind." (Lewis, 1972)

According to the psychiatrist Eugene Blueler, the question of whether an illness is caused by psychological or physical causes is not the real issue in most cases. He said, "You need always to consider, not what of this is mental or physical–the two invariably go together." (Lewis, Howard and Martha, 1972) Skin acne, for instance, often coincides with problems of self-image; acne often occurs in the teenage years when a young person has difficulty adjusting to or accepting his or her body image. It is impossible to say that either the self image problem or the acne is the most important, because both express the same process; acne merely expresses the inner turmoil caused by feelings of being misunderstood and unappreciated.

Much of our problem in dealing with illness comes from a misuse of our language. We speak of an illness using words and images that categorize illness as a separation of body and mind, rather than as the one process it is. We have created a mind-body separation by our failure to recognize and use the original body language of illness. To resolve this artificial separation, we need to speak of and visualize an illness as the symbolic expression of one process of conflict. We can best do this by using the symbolic body language of illness that already exists, waiting to be heard.

It is likely you are used to thinking of yourself as physical and mental. This distinction does not reflect what you really are, and comes from a false use of language. Your "mind" and "body" are actually integrated parts of your whole. It is impossible for one part of you to change without affecting or changing the other parts simultaneously. If you feel fear at a scary movie, your body reacts by producing stress-related hormones to help you fight or flee.

Graham and a Language of Body-Mind Unity

The scientist David Graham saw the body-mind problem as the result of using language that separates two aspects of one event, thus causing us to speak of one illness event as two processes rather than one. Graham realized that the way we speak of an illness determines how we perceive it. If we speak of the physical and mental processes as separate, we also perceive body and mind as separate. Graham said, "The difference between mental and physical is not in the event observed, but in the language in which it is discussed." (Graham, 1967) "Actually," says Dr. Graham, "few physicians disagree with the idea that the mind and body influence each other."

Graham believed that it is not enough to honor the interrelationship between body and mind. There is a need to use language that describes what is happening to an individual as one holistic process. Graham gave many examples of how people use language to continue this body-mind separation. One such example was from a medical text that stated, "In hysteria we deal with persons with healthy bodies." (Graham, 1967) What is forgotten in these statements is that mental and physical processes are two sides of the same coin.

The body language of illness that already exists can be used by both medical professionals and lay people. This language can help medical personnel and the ill person to communicate with each other and to better understand the important conflict that needs to be healed. To use this language accurately, the patient needs to be viewed as the best source of the nature of the inner conflict symbolized by illness. The patient needs to explore the archetypal symbolic meanings behind bodily symptoms and how they apply to his or her life. The symptoms of stiffness, inflexibility and over-defensiveness of arthritis, for instance, can give the arthritic a clue that somewhere in his or her life there is a conflict that expresses similar mental, emotional and spiritual attitudes. If this language is used in kind, exploratory ways to discover the conflict behind an illness, it can help bring understanding, hope and healing.

To use language to speak of illness as one process, it is necessary to not rely on the technical jargon of medicine or science, but to speak a clear language that can be easily understood by all involved. This language is based on the awareness that the body is constantly adapting to our unbalanced states, and in this reaction is a metaphor for the mental-emotional-spiritual conflict that underlies it. For instance, in speaking of a case of duodenal ulcer, you could say, "An ulceration of the duodenal is present that expresses Mr. J.'s belief and feeling that he is deprived of what is due him, that he wants to get even, and that he feels out of control despite struggle and exhaustion related to feelings of alienation from God, life and others."

Holistic Approaches Include More Than "Scientific Approaches"

By speaking of an illness as a metaphor for deeper conflict, the ill person takes the responsibility and freedom that comes with healing. Traditional medicine prides itself on taking a rational, reasonable approach to illness, but at the same time its approach does not meet several of the requirements of scientific, rational thought. These are to have complete and adequate information, and to control and predict the variables. Traditional medicine dismisses or devalues the place of emotions such as fear, anger, despair, and spiritual alienation in the creation and healing of disease. The individual who fears for his survival and feels unsupported by an unfriendly universe is more likely to develop back problems, for instance, than someone with no insecurities.

In its efforts to be rational and scientific, traditional medicine has given little or no recognition to the power of intuitive, synergistic knowledge–the spontaneous correct knowledge of the meaning of an illness that is possible for every ill individual. Unfortunately, the body language of illness cannot be fully understood without using a synthesis of both hemispheres of the mind. Western medicine and civilization has depended entirely upon the left hemispheres of our brains. This left hemisphere favors a perception of separation, in contrast to the more holistic perception of the right hemisphere.

The left hemisphere of the brain contains the speech center and controls the right half of the body. This center uses the logic and reasoning of linear thinking to arrive at assessments or conclusions. It focuses on what is most easily measurable in terms of the senses. Since feelings such as anger, hate, and despair are not easily measured, more concrete physical things such as blood or urine are measured and valued instead. The left brain sees the "bits" or "parts," and the cause and effect relationships between them, rather than the whole interacting picture. Anything that can not readily be perceived or measured is not considered valuable. The left brain sees the world as being separate from itself, and therefore not connected to the whole. Its style is more active and masculine.

The right hemisphere operates differently than the left. Its language is through metaphors and images rather than words. It knows through intuition what the totality of the picture is, and also has a sense of what something comes from and where it may go. The right brain (unlike the left) can understand paradoxes, ambiguities and opposites. It takes in the whole of an illness or event, rather than focusing on its parts. It can simultaneously receive and feel what it experiences. The right hemisphere compares through metaphor rather than measurement.

The reason we are not more successful in healing illnesses is because the masculinized, left-brained culture and medicine of the Western world has devalued right hemisphere function and experience. As a result, we as individuals and as a culture have suffered. Our Western civilization and medicine have allowed one half of our brains–our left hemispheres–to repress and dominate the intuitive perceptions of the right hemispheres. To get a fully balanced understanding of an illness, we need a balanced synthesis of both the left and right hemispheres working together.

When I am doing a holistic assessment, I have come to anticipate that any ill person, if willing, is able to come to a spontaneous correct intuitive understanding of the meaning of an illness. That knowledge can then be used to make rational changes in his or her life. Healing an illness requires a willingness to trust all parts of yourself–your feelings, intuition, body and intellect–so one can come to a conscious understanding of the dynamics of an illness. I foresee a time in the future when healing an illness will require more than disease specialists; it will require health specialists who can help people understand the unified process of an illness and its healing, and how healing can occur through resolving inner conflict.

It is not enough to create a language that defines the illness process; we also have to speak about and visualize a process of healing. This can be done by creating ideals to replace dysfunctional beliefs. One such ideal for a Type A personality with heart disease could be the Chinese proverb: "He who is hurried cannot walk gracefully." (Friedman and Ulmer, 1984) The teenager with acne may benefit just as much from dealing with problems of self-image as from medicine.

The Scientific Basis of Body-Mind Unity

Traditional medicine is just beginning to recognize that we create our illnesses and to acknowledge the enormous capacity for self-healing this gives us. The science of the interconnections between the body and the mind is called psychobiology, or psychoneuroimmunology; "psycho-" for mind, "neuro-" for nervous system, and "immuno-" for the immune system. The greatest breakthroughs in medical science in the future will come in discovering the complex ways that the psyche and the body interact to keep us healthy or to make us sick. The brain secretes at least four hundred complex chemical substances including hormones, neurotransmitters and endorphins that carry messages back and forth between the mind and body. Most of these compounds are called neuropeptides or peptides.

Glands in the head which affect the endocrine, immune and lymphatic systems of the body release peptides in response to mental, emotional, and spiritual beliefs and attitudes. These peptides or neurotransmitters carry the messages of our thoughts and emotions to our bodies. They give our bodies information such as "relax," "fight," "make more of this"; they direct our immune cells to help us cope with our perceived conflicts. This information system is two way; our immune cells actually make peptides in order to send messages back to the brain.

As early as 1937, Geoffrey Harris, a British scientist, proposed a revolutionary theory that explained the link between the emotions, mind and body. Harris theorized that the endocrine and nervous systems were one functional unit with the hypothalamus as the control center. He believed the hypothalamus serves the purpose of transmitting all the messages from the brain via the pituitary to the body. Harris suggested that the hypothalamus manufactures and secretes chemicals that flow into the pituitary and thereby allows the nervous system to modify pituitary outputs. He recognized that a vast array of informational networks from all over the brain converge on the hypothalamus. Harris' theory was later proven by Schally and Guillemin who shared a Nobel prize in 1977 for their discovery of chemicals manufactured by the hypothalamus.

Harris' theory explained scientifically how each person can control what happens to his or her body by changing the emotional, mental, and spiritual states that lead to an illness. He proved that every emotional state has a chemical reaction which accompanies it. On a practical level, we can recognize that prolonged or intense emotional states such as rage, despair, depression, anxiety, fear, or grief cause the brain to undergo specific biochemical changes which affect the organs or nerves that symbolize our conflicts. The trauma of seeing too much violence can, for instance, lead to blindness. Several hundred Cambodian refugees in the United States have gone blind, apparently because they did not want to see more death, violence and suffering. Despite the fact that there is no physical damage to their eyes that could explain their blindness, they cannot see. Psychiatrists would dismiss their blindness as "conversion reactions." I believe all illnesses are some form of symbolic conversion of a conflict that is not resolved on the mental, emotional, or spiritual level.

Clues to the Meaning of the Body Language of Illness in Cliches

Cliches are expressions such as "get off my back" that have been used so often that they have become commonplace. There are two kinds of language the body uses; the primary symbolic language of the body, and these common expressions. Both languages use the function or activity of the body. Common cliches relate to both healthy relationships, like "standing on your own feet," and unhealthy ones like "I can't stomach that." The cliches that speak of some dysfunction of the body are helpful, because they give us insight and help us understand the meaning of an illness or bodily symptom. The cliches in *Table 1* have to do with a destructive posture of the body. These cliches help us understand the mental, emotional and spiritual attitudes behind a symptom or illness.

Table 1		
Body Part Attitude	Cliche of the Body	Emotional-Mental-Spiritual
head	"hard headed"	obstinate, opinionated
neck	"stiff-necked"	stubborn, unchanging
forehead	"highbrow"	snobbish
hands	"tight-fisted"	stingy, grasping
face	"shame-faced"	humiliated or self-effacing
chin	"chin up"	suppressing grief or fear
lips	"tight-lipped"	judgemental
mouth	"close-mouthed"	incommunicative
jaw	"setting one's jaw"	defiant
teeth	"coming to grips"	confronting
	"getting a bite on it"	aggressive action
voice	"having no voice"	loss of status or significance
shoulders	"shouldering others' burdens"	taking others' responsibilities

Body Part	Cliche of the Body	Emotional-Mental-Spiritual Attitude
back	"get off my back"	anger at aggression
	"getting back up"	fear at some situation
	"backed against the wall"	feeling cut off or limited
heart	"hard-hearted"	insensitive to feelings
	"broken-hearted"	rejected in love
stomach	"unable to stomach"	inability to process
elbows	"elbows up"	aggressive attitude
	"elbow way in"	aggressive actions
arms	"up in arms"	defensive
gallbladder	"that galls me"	angry response
skin	"touchy"	overly sensitive
	"out of touch"	unconnected
knees	"weak-kneed"	afraid, without courage
	"knock-kneed"	inflexible
feet	"no standing"	lacking a place, uprooted

Transforming the Negative Ego

It is important to see that illness is the end result of negative, destructive patterns within us–of a negative ego that is no less real than other, more positive ones. If you can discover and transform these negative patterns into more positive ones, then you can answer the message of an illness and heal it. The parts of you that created an unhealthy, dull, boring or unsuccessful life are immature parts that are less than what they can be. You give these parts permission to take over and make you unhappy and unhealthy when you refuse to think, feel and act in fully responsible, adult ways. These immature parts are the child, adolescent, or critical parent that act under the direction of your negative ego. The irresponsible adolescent part of yourself, for instance, can take over, and by refusing to be responsible for how you live your life, what you eat, or how you use your energy, can lead to a malfunctioning pancreas and to diabetes.

The ego is supposed to be only a message taker from our outer reality. It becomes negative when instead of doing its job it begins to run on negative patterns from the past. Instead of merely handling what is before it, the ego evaluates everything in terms of negative thoughts and beliefs. It is important not to be afraid of the negative ego and to see it as a weak part of ourselves. If we can recognize these patterns, we can refuse to listen to them. We can deny them, choosing more positive beliefs. The negative ego makes us sick because it is disoriented, alienated and leads us to our failure. One of the patterns or "tapes" the negative ego loves to play is the one that says, "Life is a struggle. Unless you are fighting, you are going to fail." This belief is then taken up by the critical parental part of you that is always looking to others to validate and bolster its self-esteem through their approval. Eventually the stress this inner conflict causes may lead to heart disease. What would happen if a person began to change this and instead believed, "Life is a gift that I need only open"?

One of the ways the negative ego avoids the responsibility of thinking and feeling is to blame human nature and to deny that we are responsible for an illness. It is common to look at an illness as some unfortunate accident of germs, heredity or environment. Medical science has just began to recognize that most illnesses are weak, puny adversaries to the powerful agents of our immune systems. Similarly, the dysfunctional belief systems of our negative egos are no competition for the powerful positive forces of love, hope and truth.

Chapter Two

Understanding the Symbolic
Messages of an Illness

The Process

One of the steps in healing ourselves is to go through a process of inquiry, seeking the symbolism of an illness. Identifying the specific attitude that expresses an illness does not have to be a mysterious, lengthy process or research project. It can be as simple as observing the illness process and asking, "How is what is happening to my body (the specific symptoms) descriptive or expressive of (a symbolic metaphor for) what is happening in my life?" or "Are there any cliches that help me understand this?" or "How are the specific functions that are ill in my body expressive of some corresponding mental, emotional or spiritual conflict in my life?"

More specifically one can ask, as one would in exploring dream symbolism, "Where in my life is what is happening to my body also happening in my attitudes, thoughts or emotions?" This kind of inquiry can be very productive if done in an objective, exploratory way. It is necessary to get beyond the names of an illness to look at what functions of the body are involved and how these express inner conflicts.

Illness as Both a Physical and Psychic Archetype

An archetype is a form or pattern that occurs naturally both in the physical and the psychic world. Everyone has the same biological apparatus–bones, skin, muscles, lungs, blood and heart–and these basic patterns are the archetypes of our biological form. At the same time, every body is unique. These physical archetypes correspond to psychic archetypes, because the physical and psychic parts of us are interwoven.

You can approach the meaning of an illness with the same openness and sense of wonder that you would in discovering the meaning of your dreams. Just as the symbolism of a dream may have a universal or archetypal meaning as well as a personal one, so the symbolism of an illness may also refer to a common area of conflict, and also how that area of conflict is expressed in your life. The symbol of a special child in a dream, for instance, suggests something new is coming into your life, but only you can know what that new idea, person or growth is.

Similarly, the illness of diabetes may mean different things to different people, though to all it has something to do with a misuse of the way energy is being used. The pancreas is the organ that deals with the storage and use of energy and can be compared to the fuel tank of a car. If you are misusing your energy or allowing others to "drain your tank," then there is not enough energy left for you. In exploring how the common meaning of the function of the pancreas applies to you, you can ask yourself such questions as: "Have I been irresponsible in the way I have been using my energy? Have I taken too little responsibility for myself, or too much for others?"

Correspondence

Correspondence is the similarity or appropriateness of some organ or function of the body to elements of the psyche. Correspondence is based upon the principle of synchronicity, which refers to the phenomenon that every natural fact is a symbol of some mental, emotional or spiritual one. Carl Jung was the first psychiatrist who spoke of this principle, but great philosophers, healers and poets down through the ages have used and understood it.

Jung defined synchronicity as "coincidences" that had meaning, events that are connected through their meaning. To illustrate this he gave the example of his experience with a patient who was overly intellectual in her approach to life. This woman had an impressive dream the night before concerning a golden scarab. While she was telling him this dream, Jung heard a noise on the window pane. He opened the window and caught a golden scarab as it flew in. He presented it to his patient, saying, "Here is your scarab." This experience helped his patient recognize the importance of the non-rational but meaningful events of life.*

Visionaries such as Jung know that everything we perceive in physical reality is a symbolic extension of processes and interactions which are going on inside us, the experiences each of us are having. They know that the synchronicity of even the smallest, seemingly insignificant event is based upon the unity behind all creation.

One of the first steps in deciphering the meaning of an illness is to look at the natural function of the part of the body that is affected by an illness. If you have had a heart attack, for instance, you can look to the function of the heart, which is to feel, especially to feel love for yourself and others. In the language of the body, a heart attack is literally an attack upon the heart brought about through the inability of an individual to process or feel his or her emotions, especially love. A heart attack is an explosion of energy attempting to break through an emotional barrier. This wall may be created by intense feelings of fear or anger that build up a pattern of control. In exploring what lies behind a heart attack, you can

---

* A scarab is a form of beetle, and golden scarabs are quite rare. The scarab is imbued with mythological or religious significance in some cultures.

begin by asking questions such as, "How have I created an emotional barrier to feelings and love, that only an explosion of energy could break through?"

Some examples of how the function or organ of the body has a symbolic correspondence to emotional and physical conflicts are presented in *Table 2*.

The function of the liver, for instance, is to purify the body by processing out toxins. Those who have liver problems are usually those who refuse to process negative emotions and who sometimes hide from these emotions through addiction to alcohol. Recovery from alcoholism requires that an alcoholic process and release negative emotions and thoughts. Alcohol affects many parts of the body. The organs which suffer the most damage often indicate the main conflicts underlying a condition (alcoholism, in this example). Problems with the liver, for instance, often relate to a refusal to process and let go of the past.

If you have an immune deficiency problem such as AIDS or cancer look at how defense*less*, how victimized, or how martyred you are. If you have an auto-immune problem, in which your immune system is attacking your body, look at how defens*ive* you are. Do you resist learning more constructive beliefs and receiving help from others or from your higher consciousness? If you have a problem with your blood, look at whether you refuse to release old shame, anger or fear from your blood relationships.

Table 2

Physical Part	Function	Mental, Emotional or Spiritual Problems
head	to think, intuit or decide	indecision, not paying attention to soul
eyes	seeing	competitiveness, not wanting to see what is in world
ears	hearing	not wanting to hear things, fear of death
throat	expression	closing things off due to fear
shoulders	carrying	carrying negative emotion
elbows	to punch or hit	holding back anger, aggression
upper back	to stand upright	belief one has too much responsibility for other people, not enough for self
digestion	processing food	difficulty processing feelings
pancreas	storage	storing negative feelings
liver	purifying	inability to let go of past
heart	feeling	having difficulty feeling or loving self and others
gall bladder	stores bile that promotes digestion	difficulty processing, e.g. anger

Physical Part	Function	Mental, Emotional or Spiritual Problems
genitals	pleasure	guilt or denial of pleasure, especially sexual pleasure
hips	staying put	stubbornness, unwillingness to change or grow
knees	bending	inflexibility, aggressive anger, lack of love of self and others
bowel or colon	elimination	diarrhea-wanting to get through something quickly
		colon-clinging to the material, energies absorbed in owning
		colitis and cancer of colon-not able to let go of negative, remembering, keeping it alive
shins	to proceed	negative emotions
thyroid	regulates metabolism	excessive or suppressed use of energy for activity or growth
ankles	to bend	inflexibility, resisting fun
hands	assertiveness or aggressiveness	problems with assertiveness, giving and receiving
feet	standing	insecurity, blaming mom or dad for lack of safety or security
skin	facing the world	difficulties over your self image and accepting it.

Correspondence of Body and Soul

Current medicine and psychology do not recognize the presence and activities of a creative soul or higher consciousness acting both within and outside the body and mind. I counsel and live by the premise that there is a soul in myself and in those I seek to help, that is of good intent and which desires to help us grow and heal ourselves. This soul is active in our bodies, especially through our nervous systems that keep our hearts and bodies functioning involuntarily. The soul is also active in our minds, especially when we enter relaxed alerted states of the subconscious mind where we can most easily access its insights.

One of the special human abilities that sets us apart from the animals is our conscious ability to heal ourselves. Animals heal themselves, but do not do this as consciously as we do. The ability to heal ourselves depends on our cooperation with our souls. Our souls form and cushion our lives. Each of us has a soul that loves us personally and wishes to communicate with us to help us grow in ways that are within our highest ideal for ourselves. Our souls speak to us in times of darkness and illness, but they would much rather speak to us daily in times of beauty and inspiration.

My experience as a counselor and individual confirms the existence of the soul. I have witnessed that a person receives information or inspiration through images, feelings and insights in a consistent way if he or she is willing and open to receive them. Souls have a wide range of ways to communicate with us; they communicate for instance with and through me as a healer in my dreams and insights when I ask for that help, as well as through the one whom I seek to heal. The soul is that part of us that reaches for the finest and best in us through cooperation with each person's individual abilities. It reacts to inner patterns and stimulates the individual to discover his or her most ideal nature.

Our souls use our feminine energy of feeling, imagination and intuition to speak to us. If we have blocked our feminine energy of imagination, our souls have to speak to us through misfortune. Since the soul and the body are interwoven and inseparable, a conflict expresses itself symbolically through bodily symptoms most related to that function of the body. The soul is both inside the body and outside it at the same time. No left-brained masculinized science or medicine can fully capture the evidence of the soul, though this evidence does have a logic of its own. That evidence comes directly through personal experience of intuition, feeling, knowing and healing.

One way to prevent illness is to invite your soul to speak to you in your daily life so it does not have to speak to you only in times of illness, pain and fear. To do this, use the language of the soul, which is imagination; not just imaging or visualizing, but by using your imagination to be inspired by your soul. Your soul loves beauty. This can come by reading or writing poetry or prose, listening to your "soul music," or being in your garden or out in nature. Create sacred places in your home or outdoors, where in meditation you can sit and invite your soul.

One of the reasons we have difficulty reflecting on the meaning of an illness is the limitations of our language. We think that if there are no words to describe something, it cannot exist or is not valuable. Our souls overcome these language limitations by speaking to us in images and symbols. If we refuse to recognize or explore the feminine language of imagination, we close off the voice of our soul and its message. If in meditation, a man receives the image of his throat cancer as a bristly pine cone, he can choose to explore his defensiveness or call the message "stupid" or "senseless." This message opens the possibility of healing by asking where did this defensiveness begin, and, most importantly, why does he still continue to bristle and defend himself.

Energy Centers and Conflicts

One helpful way to understand the meaning of an illness is to look at the conflict issue of the energy center near it. There are focal points in the body where certain conflict issues find expression in illness. These energy centers are traditionally known as chakras, the ancient Eastern name for a wheel or vortex of energy. Each of these energy centers correspond to important issues of growth or conflict. The issue for the first chakra located at the tail bone is that of security, of the genital area is pleasure, of the solar plexus is emotional control, of the heart center is love, of the throat center is expression, of the brow is intuition, and of the top of the head is spirituality.

Chakras can be seen as spheres or disks spinning in all directions. Our chakras are the doorways to universal energy that allow our bodies to move, touch, feel, smell, hear, see and be alive in our reality. This energy is always around us. When there is some kind of illness, we have created blockages by our thoughts or feelings that stop this universal energy from reaching and flowing through us freely. When these energy centers are receptive or going inward, it is predominately yin or feminine. When these energy centers are active or moving outward, they are predominately masculine or yang in energy. Our bodies need to be simultaneously both yin and yang, in balance, to be healthy.

These energy centers and their related issues are repeated upon both the arms and legs. Conflicts with security, for instance, are correspondingly repeated on the hands and feet. Conflicts with pleasure are repeated upon the wrists and ankles, and so on, as indicated in *Figure 1*, on the following page.

These conflict issues are related traditionally to colors. The first chakra is associated with red, the second with orange, the third with yellow, the fourth with green, the fifth with blue, the sixth with indigo and the seventh with violet or white. The odd numbered chakras are predominantly masculine in energy, and the even numbered ones predominantly feminine, with the seventh chakra being a balance of both.

One of the most comprehensive and reliable systems of relating the chakras of the body to certain important issues of growth and development is that of Lazaris. I have found his system both accurate and helpful in understanding the issues behind an illness and understanding their broader meaning. The predominant

Chakra Body Energy Issues and Centers

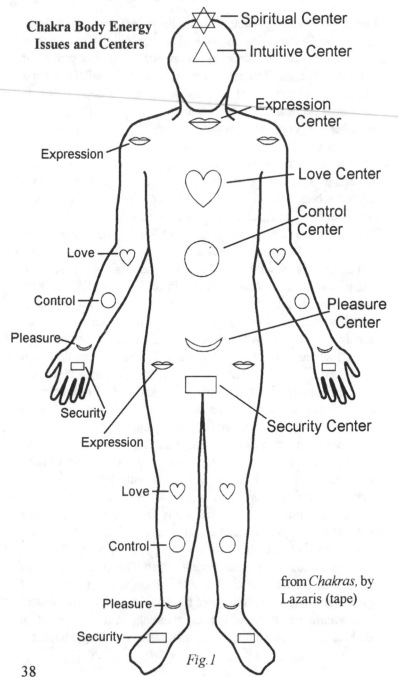

Spiritual Center

Intuitive Center

Expression Center

Expression

Love Center

Control Center

Love

Control

Pleasure Center

Pleasure

Security

Expression

Security Center

Love

Control

Pleasure

Security

from *Chakras*, by Lazaris (tape)

Fig. 1

38

issues by which illness is related to the chakra systems of the body is summarized and given in *Figure 1*.

The issue of the first chakra, located at the coccyx/tail bone at the back of the body projecting to the front below the navel and above the genitals, is that of security. This kind of energy level deals with all issues related to security in our relationships to the earth and others as well as to the spiritual. In the lower body this is expressed in the feet; in the upper body in the hand; and in the whole body in the lower back, tail bone, anus and colon. Illnesses of the energy system related to security affect the feet, hands, rectum and tail bone.

Dysfunctions in the area of the first chakra have to do with a lack of safety and unresolved fear or anxiety. Some of the illnesses related to this chakra area are chronic lower back pain, sciatica, and rectal difficulties including cancer and tumors. People who have illnesses in first chakra areas tend to believe their world is unsafe. Any growth that helps a person feel more secure affects the health of this area of the body. If a person has an illness in the first chakra area, he or she can explore whether or not there is a conflict about feelings of insecurity and an imbalance in masculine energies.

The second chakra corresponds to all energies related to pleasure, from sexual pleasure to pleasure from a relationship to our higher self or God/ Goddess/All There Is. In the lower body this energy is expressed in the ankles, in the upper body in the wrists, in the whole body from the knees down to the ankles, and in the torso in the testes of men and the ovaries of women. Illnesses related to not allowing pleasure into your life affect the wrists, genitals, pelvic area and ankles (such as sprained ankles and problems with the Achilles' tendon).

The issue of the second chakra is power or sexual struggle versus enjoyment or pleasure in our relationships to life, others or the creator. People with conflicts in the sexual or relationship area tend to see relationships in terms of struggle rather than pleasure, and domination rather than cooperation and the pleasure that comes from it. Illnesses related to this chakra are all the female and male dysfunctions such as menstrual, uterine or prostate problems, pelvic and lower back pain, bladder, urinary and kidney problems.

The third chakra is located in the solar plexus and corresponds to all energies related to control or co-creation, from problems related to manipulation and domination to those related to allowing co-creation to occur with God/Goddess/All There Is. In the lower body, issues related to control are expressed in the calves of the legs, in the upper body in the forearms, and in the whole body from the knee to the thigh. Illness related to problems of control of your life affect the calves, forearms, stomach and solar plexus area. Central to this issue is whether you trust or have confidence in yourself to direct your life consciously, or whether you either dominate or over-control yourself or allow others to do so. Self-confidence is essential to health as is the self-respect that comes with exercising your personal power without struggle. Dysfunctions of the gallbladder, pancreas, adrenal glands, spleen, colon, intestines, stomach and liver are related to this area. This chakra is often related to conflicts concerning power and the inability to express anger and fear at feeling powerless to meet our needs cleanly. Arthritis, kidney and immune deficiency disorders such as chronic fatigue syndrome, Epstein-Barr and other autoimmune disorders often originate in this area.

The fourth chakra is located in the heart area and corresponds to all energies related to love, from survival and self-love to cosmic love. In the lower body, issues related to love are expressed in the knees, in the upper body in the elbows, and in the whole body in the pelvic girdle. Illnesses that are related to problems of love in all its forms are those of the heart and lungs, elbows, knees, and pelvic girdle. Some of the illnesses related to this chakra are heart attack, enlarged heart, asthma, allergies, lung problems, bronchial pneumonia, and upper back and shoulder problems.

The fifth chakra is located in the throat area and corresponds to all energies related to expression of all the issues of the chakras below: the expression of security, pleasure, control and love. In the lower body, issues related to expression are symbolized in the pelvic area. In the upper body, expression is symbolized in the shoulders and upper torso; and in the whole body, from the abdominal area to the neck. Illnesses related to problems of expression are those that affect the throat, the shoulders and upper torso, the pelvic girdle and also the thyroid gland.

The central issue of the fifth chakra is expression in relationship to exerting our will through such expression. Problems with the thyroid, esophagus, neck, throat and teeth are related to this area. Fears of personal expression, ridicule or criticism are important to understanding the imbalances of this area. Various addictions such as to drugs, alcohol, food, and cigarettes are related to problems in this chakra. These addictions reflect a conflict in expressing our willpower, needs and feelings openly and effectively.

The sixth chakra, located only in the forehead, is the intuitive center and corresponds to all energies related to psychic, intuitive and metaphysical abilities. Illnesses related to this area are headaches and those affecting the pituitary gland.

The issue of the sixth chakra is that of intuition and active thinking. This issue is related to whether or not we allow ourselves to be open to and to receive our intuition and inner wisdom and intelligence. A refusal to be receptive or introspective can block this chakra. Illnesses related to this chakra are brain tumors, strokes, neurological disorders, blindness, deafness, spinal difficulties, migraine and tension headaches, anxiety, nervousness, nervous breakdowns, depression, schizophrenia and epilepsy.

The seventh chakra, the spiritual center, is located at the top of the head and corresponds to all energies related to our relationship to God/Goddess/All There Is. This center is located only at the top of the head at the third eye center* (pineal gland) connected to the optic nerve. Illnesses of the head are often related to this center. The seventh chakra or spiritual chakra is related to finding a broader spiritual meaning in existence and to having a cooperative relationship with your higher power or God/Goddess/All There Is. The broader perception that is possible with the opening

---

*We are aware that other systems have placed the third eye in the forehead.

of this chakra is related to the understanding that comes from the effective use and resolution of the issues of all the other chakras.

If you have an illness and wish to explore its meaning, it is helpful to ask how the main issues related to that area of the body concern you. For instance, if you have a heart condition it is important to explore issues related to love. How compassionate have you been to yourself? Have you taken the time to really become intimate with yourself and those around you? Are you doing those things in your life that are loving to yourself and others around you? By addressing the major issues related to a chakra system, one can come closer to the hidden message of an illness, so that message can be answered.

In his book, *The Healing Heart*, Norman Cousins tells the story of his recovery from a heart attack that resulted from coronary heart disease. The question of whether or not he had made his love known to his loved ones haunted Cousins during the crucial twenty-four hours after his heart attack. Just prior to his heart attack, Cousins had traveled almost constantly and had had little opportunity to engage in sports or physical recreation or to see his immediate family.

Cousins had just returned from a hectic trip to the East Coast, only to discover that he was due to leave again in a few days for the Southeast. He had considered the possibility of postponement or cancellation of his trip because of his fatigue. The day after he had reviewed the facts that made it essential to go through with his engagements, and had made the decision that only the most drastic event would get him out of it, he had his heart attack. People who feel locked into obligations that they would rather set aside are candidates for sudden and serious disease, according to Arnold Hutschnecker in his book *The Will to Live*. The issue of self-love and love of others is central to the hidden meaning of heart disease.

Specific Attitudes Symbolized by Illness

Franz Alexander was the first to propose the theory that there were specific identifiable attitudes expressive of any illness. Other pioneers have researched and proven that there are specific attitudes expressive of heart disease, including Dr. Friedman and his associates who identified the relationship between Type A behavior and heart disease. What is most exciting of all about their work is how they used the knowledge concerning Type A personality to later *modify* Type A personality and to prevent further heart attacks in those who changed their personality patterns.

This research, and the work of Doctor David Graham with specific attitudes related to illness, has profound implications for what can be done to heal illnesses. Graham, Woolf and others have noted that there is a correspondence or a similarity between what happens in the body and the specific conflicted attitude that a sick individual holds. One example Graham gives of this similarity is that which is present in those who suffer from asthma and hay fever.

He views asthma as just a more intense, extreme case of hay fever or vasomotor rhinitis. In both illnesses there is a reaction of the mucous membranes to a noxious agent so as to exclude it by swelling of the membrane with consequent narrowing of the passageways, and diluting it and washing it out by hypersecretion. In hay fever or vasomotor rhinitis these changes are limited to the nose. When these changes are more acute and sufficiently intense to include the bronchial tubes, so that wheezing occurs, this illness is called "asthma."

Graham points out that the physical symptoms of asthma and hay fever occur when an individual is facing a situation with the wish that he did not have to do anything about it, or that it would go away, or that someone else would take over the responsibility. The essential feature of this attitude is the desire to have nothing to do with the situation at all, to deal with it by excluding it. Typical statements were these: "I wanted them to go away," "I didn't want to have anything to do with it," "I wanted to blot it all out."

Graham recognized that the specific attitude accompanying an illness is descriptive or expressive of the bodily function with which it is associated. Just as the body of the asthmatic is trying to wash out and exclude a noxious substance from the body, so the asthmatic is trying to rid himself of or to deny some noxious situation in his life. The inner attitude that is present simultaneously with the physical symptoms symbolizes the inner conflict.

Some evidence that supports the research of Graham and his associates concerning specific attitudes of disease suggests ways that healing can occur through reprogramming and befriending the subconscious minds of sick individuals. Under hypnosis, patients with histories of and a predisposition toward certain diseases can be coaxed into attacks or symptoms merely by suggesting these attitudes to them or reminding them of the attitudes. For example, an asthma patient told to feel unloved, rejected, or shut out while under hypnosis will experience an asthma attack. Even more fascinating is that even people in good health sometimes respond to specific suggestions by developing the expected physical symptoms. Under hypnosis, someone with normal blood pressure when told to be on guard, alert to danger and ready for anything will experience a modest elevation of blood pressure.

Resolving the Mental-Emotional-Spiritual Conflicts Behind Our Illnesses

Physical illness is a valuable feedback system that helps us be honest as to what our conflicts are and where we are in our overall growth. In any illness, there is a conflict of beliefs and their related feelings that prevent the realization of our needs for safety, pleasure, control, love, intuition and spirituality. When conflict is present, our basic needs for safety, the pleasure of belonging, the conscious creation of our lives, love for ourselves and others, our understanding of life, and our sense of unity with all there is, have been blocked. Some belief, or more likely a complex or web of beliefs, keeps us from growing. A complex is a system of

44

associated ideas by which we try to understand our reality. This complex is destructive when it conflicts with or contradicts our needs.

For each body there is an ideal called the etheric pattern. This pattern for each of us is free from conflict, open to relaxation, happiness and the fulfillment of needs and preferences. The resolution of a conflict begins with the awareness of it and then with the process of discovering the series of related ideas and their emotions that are beneath the illness. Janice, who had problems with an inactive immune system and related illnesses such as candidiasis (candida) and chronic fatigue, had the following series of ideas: (1) The world is an unfriendly place. (2) I need to be perfect to be on top of it. (3) I am not good enough. (4) No matter how hard I struggle, I will never be good enough. (5) I am sick and tired of struggling, but there is no other way.

When you are aware of the nature of the beliefs underlying an illness, it is then necessary to define beliefs that are positive opposites and that will lead to the condition you wish to achieve. It is not enough just to have an intellectual understanding of your negative pattern. The negative belief or complex of beliefs behind this illness needs to be replaced by direct concise statements. In Janice's case, the following beliefs were built into her conscious and subconscious mind: (1) Every day I am becoming more and more aware of the world as a friendly place to be. (2) It is all right for me to make mistakes, because that is how I learn and grow as a creative person. (3) I am good enough and a valuable person. (4) There is always a way to do things in a pleasurable, happy way. (5) I will seek and find the happier way, with the help of my Higher Self. Using imagery, Janice also lifted the cloak of perfectionism she carried upon her shoulders. Soon after, her immune system was tested and found to be functioning normally.

The reprogramming of your conscious and subconscious is done by quieting your body and mind, then repeating the statement or statements that are opposite to your past destructive beliefs every day for at least ten to fifteen minutes or until they are part of your consciousness and actions. *As much time needs to be spent*

45

*ion opposite, more healthy beliefs and their related
feelings as is done in imaging physical healing of bodily symptoms.* Remember these physical symptoms are only symbols of the
conflicts your beliefs and choices create. Mental, emotional and
spiritual reprogramming is just as important as physical healing.

You also have to be willing to do all the things necessary to
bring about your good health. If you discover that the root of your
illness is a pervasive anxiety that masks fear, face your specific
fears (for instance, fear of loneliness and abandonment) and do
those courageous things which counteract it. Your decision to live
and get well is critical. This has to replace any prognosis you may
have been given by medical authorities. *You* make the rules for
your body; no one else *can.* Reprogramming always needs to be
followed by a willingness to follow your inner guidance as to what
steps–mental, emotional, physical and spiritual–need to be taken
to bring you into balance. Quiet yourself and ask, "What do my
soul and Higher Self wish to tell me through this illness? What
steps do I need to take next to become more healthy?"

One of the first questions you can explore concerning a belief
or belief complex is whether it is necessary. Beliefs based upon a
false sense of guilt, or "I should" beliefs are destructive. If you are
feeling guilty about something, such as sexuality, that harms no
one including yourself, then you can eliminate the "I should"
beliefs concerning it as unnecessary. You may also have to
eliminate religious beliefs that associate sexuality with sin; such
beliefs are neither spiritual, nor healthy. Conflicts based upon
"shoulds" such as these need to be replaced with beliefs that allow
you to fulfill your needs. Questions that may help create new
beliefs are: "Why should I feel guilty about experiencing sexual
pleasure with my husband?" "Why should I always be perfect?"
"Why should I expect others to understand me when I do not speak
up for myself or express my desires and needs?"

Another way to heal an illness is to remember it is not the
illness itself that is your primary focus of concern. The illness
represents symbolically some area of conflict within yourself that
you have denied, discounted, distracted and defended yourself

against. Processing and programming an illness is bringing this unconscious conflict into consciousness where you can use all the special human abilities of choice, imagination, intelligence and love to heal yourself. The common practice of evaluating illness as something beyond your conscious control is emotionally exhausting and weakens even more an already compromised immune system. By focusing upon the resolution of your underlying conflict, you take control of an illness and are not a victim of it.

There is nothing more helpful in resolving a conflict than forgiving yourself or others. You can resolve a conflict within yourself or with others by increasing your tolerance and not expecting either yourself or others to be perfect. People often confuse forgiveness with forgetting what happened. You are not forgiving what was done to you, but why it was done. To forgive does not require you to forget, but to pardon the offender.

It helps to explore whether you have within you some of the faults of your offender; for instance, low self-esteem, need to control, fear of intimacy, or a need to dominate others. This pardon may be made on the basis that this person was imperfect in his or her judgement or did not know enough. Forgiveness allows you to reclaim the energy wasted by revenge or seeking punishment. It does not matter if the other person acknowledges your forgiveness, for it is you alone who benefits from and is healed by it in being freed from your inner conflict.

How Mental-Emotional Conflicts
Manifest Physical Illness

The process by which images or beliefs held in the mind cause illness is an intricate one. This process causes muscular and cellular changes which begin when a mental-emotional-spiritual conflict generates nervous impulses and hormonal changes that cause muscles to tense. These muscular reactions in turn create blockages in the natural flow of energy in our bodies. Emotions cause movements of energy through our bodies. When these are positive emotions of an expanding nature, such as love, they cause a release of and expansion of energy.

With the so called "negative" emotional energies, such as anger, your body tenses to attack or withdraw in fear. Acute or prolonged fear or anger causes bodily energies to tense, close off and become blocked like a pinched hose which constricts the flow of energy or water through it.

Ideas and their related emotions become negative or disease-producing when they are strong or held onto persistently. Thoughts of revenge and punishment produce anger, for instance, that can be positive if it is processed and released appropriately. This means you express anger to yourself or those close to you in a way that will harm neither you or others. You do not necessarily need to express anger or fear directly to the offending person. What is important is that beliefs and feelings be expressed honestly and appropriately, so they are released from your body.

It is never enough just to release emotions; every emotion is deeply rooted in spiritual and mental beliefs. Recognize an illness is challenging you to bring up from your subconscious the conflict within you. Conflicts are resolved only when we replace destructive, inappropriate beliefs with those that challenge us to grow. Begin always with the courageous choice to think and feel. This is done first by quieting yourself and being scrupulously honest with yourself. If this conflict does not come through you into consciousness, it will come at you as fate–which may be further or more severe illness. To heal, think of yourself as a co-creator who is responsible to do your part. You get the help you ask for within and without as you take more and more responsibility to reduce the underlying conflict beneath an illness. What you are becoming, a healthy person, is more important than what you were, a sick person. The negativity that is often at the root of illness does not come from the world, it comes from you being unfriendly to yourself. However, you can resolve the conflict and change your negativity. You can give yourself the healing you deserve to receive that reflects your strength, health and self mastery.

What Payoffs am I Getting from this Illness?

Crucial to healing is your decision to give up the benefits illness gives you, such as attention, avoidance of responsibility or special care, so you can accept the greater benefits of health. You will need to reprogram your subconscious mind with the knowledge that health has more to offer you than illness. Part of healing requires one to confront oneself with the important question, "What payoffs am I getting from this illness that are unhealthy to me?"

A payoff is a hidden agenda; something you value more than what you say you want, such as happiness or health. A payoff is like a bribe you take under the table without knowing how destructive it is. A payoff becomes a poison when you think you cannot live without it and are addicted to it. You can become addicted to self-pity, for instance, just as some people are addicted to heroin, when it becomes so much a part of your life that you think you cannot live without it.

There are seven common payoffs that become poisons when people think they cannot live without them. These payoff shape your identity when they determine what you think, feel and do. These payoffs are as follows:

1. *Avoidance.* "I want to avoid something such as responsibility, happiness, intimacy, power or responsibility. What am I avoiding?"

2. *Righteousness.* "I don't want to deal with it or find solutions, instead I choose to be righteous." You can tell whether you are being righteous by where you put your emotions. Would you rather be righteous than honest or well?

3. *Blame.* "Look what they did to me!" "Who do I really want to punish?"

4. *Guarantee.* "I won't change until you guarantee things will be better." "Promise me if I change it won't hurt." "I don't believe I deserve it."

5. *Self-Pity.* "Poor me! I am not responsible for my life." There are three forms of self-pity. The victim who says people do not love him or her enough, the martyr who feels misunderstood and over-burdened, and self-pity itself as a defense against oppression, abuse and responsibility.

6. *Self-Importance.* "I'm a special case."

7. *Clinging To The Past,* trying to vindicate, relive or redo it. "If I give up trying to perfect my old destructive patterns and forgive myself, I cannot use it as an excuse to myself or others for why I am sick or unhappy." Am I living past destructive scripts over again, because I think I can do them better? Am I ashamed to admit I made some mistakes and need to forgive myself? (Lazaris, *Creating a New Play* (Tape))

Society encourages us to feel sorry for sick people. Sickness is one way people who feel self-pity can gain acceptance. By getting sick, you can expect people to give you attention you felt you could not get in other ways. To overcome self-pity, ask what impact this payoff has on those who are closest to you. Do I use my illness to demand attention or to manipulate others? This manipulation may foster resentment, rather than love. Illness may get you attention, but it prevents you from being powerful, happy and self-realized. Ask yourself what it is it you value more than your health.

Chapter Three

The Healing Process

The Relationship Between the Healer and Patient

Healing is a creative process that can be a joyful discovery; it need not be difficult. We tend to place great emphasis upon the physical aspects of an illness, but much more is involved; we must heal all those aspects of ourselves that cause us to feel that we have failed or have been alienated, disoriented, and disordered. All healing is self-healing, and a healer can make this process easier, more exciting, and less painful. As a counselor, I help people return to the process of good health from the structure of illness. I help them suspend the process of an illness long enough for them to return to good health. The body is geared to health and survival; if left to its own resources, after the mental-emotional-spiritual process underlying an illness has been suspended, the body will return to good health.

A healer creates an atmosphere of trust and an ambiance in which a person can make the decision and take the opportunity to heal him- or herself. There is no set amount of time for this process to take place; it can take a moment or many years. The sick person has to decide how much time is needed to make the changes that release an illness. The good healer provides catalysts for this change such as medicine, massage, imagery, music, color, wise

51

guidance and direction to help people change what they wish to change. The determination by both the healer and the sick person that they are not helpless and that they can together find a solution and can get help for the healing is important. Even if no apparent solution for the problem is offered by traditional medicine, where there is trust in the sick person's power to find a solution, one can always be found. That solution often lies not in traditional medicine, but in the realm of using the powerful feminine energies of feelings and healing imagery.

Healing can be joyful when the sick individual uses the power of his or her will to focus upon what is desired and to ask help in obtaining this, rather than using willpower where force and manipulation is required. Healing always requires an inner change as well as an outer one–usually in the direction of greater love and acceptance of oneself or others. There are many forms of healing that work upon the physical body–traditional medicine, homeopathic medicine, acupuncture–all of which can be helpful in addition to holistic self-healing. There is no inherent conflict between good medical treatment of any kind and intelligent self-care that deals with the mental, emotional and spiritual causes of an illness.

There are many ways to avoid assuming the responsibility for an illness, but they always deter real progress in self-healing. We can say an illness is the result of a virus, bad luck, carcinogens in the air or water, fate, or poor genes. These are all comfortable ways of evading the fact that only a limited percentage of the population seems to be affected by such influences. (LeShan, 1986) Why is it then that some workers in an office or factory catch the cold or virus "that is going around" while others do not, although all are exposed to it? Why do some 10-20% of the population never get any kind of an illness? It is a startling fact that medical records indicate that 70% of all medical treatment and surgical procedures are administered to only 30% of the population. Most of us are exposed to the same hazards of viruses, stresses, and polluted air and water, but only about 1/3 of us become ill. The other 2/3 of our population stay healthy despite nearly identical environmental stresses. (Dudley and Welke, 1977)

Steps in Healing an Illness

The *first* step in healing an illness is to express how you feel about being ill; get in touch with your feelings of anger, hurt, betrayal, fear, self-pity, depression and despair until you have expressed them so many times that you are done with them. You need to express these feelings over and over to get them out. It is not wise to pretend that they are not there. By getting in touch with the full range of your feelings, you can release them from your body. What matters is not how you should feel about an illness, but how you actually do feel. Some people find that they actually have welcomed an illness because they thought they could not face their conflicts in any other way.

The *second* step in healing is to get angry at the sickness–not apologetic for being sick–seeing it as a destructive process that you wish to release from your life. The *third* step is to forgive yourself for the illness–to apologize and accept yourself, and to go through a process of forgiveness so your healing can proceed without guilt. The *fourth* step is to make the decision to fight the sickness. To do this, educate yourself on the details of your illness, learn how you created it and what you need to do emotionally, mentally, spiritually, and physically to be free of it. Fighting an illness may involve a radical change in your life.

The *fifth* step is the one on which this book focuses –listening to the messages of your illness. This step requires that you take the time to look beneath the sickness and ask, "Why did I create this illness? What has it done to me?" Any process of healing must include a process of self-awareness that comes with listening to the messages of your illness. Jung stated, "When an inner situation is not made conscious, it appears outside as fate." In healing, the issue is the awareness that a particular belief structure and its associated emotions and attitudes is both destructive and conscious. What we think not only affects what we feel, it simultaneously affects our body. Our bodies try to serve us, to adapt to our beliefs and to find a balance within the context of what we believe. We set the rules for our bodies and if those rules are harsh, destructive ones, our bodies express this.

I have found it helpful in working with patients to first assess the process by which they created their illness, to define the thoughts and feelings typical of that disease process, and to determine how these attitudes are expressed in each individual. To help see the disease process as a unified one, I help the individual complete two circular diagrams divided into four sections, each piece representing the various aspects of an illness. Each circle is like a pie cut in quarters with a place left in the center for the central energy or ideal (see *Figures 2 & 3*, on the next 2 pages). The Illness Circle in *Figure 2* defines the illness as a holistic process created by the sick person; in the middle is the central energy or belief. The Wellness Circle (*Figure 3*) replaces the dysfunctional process of an illness with ideals and beliefs that are more healthy and are often the opposite of those causing the illness.

Immediately following the completion of the first circle, which individualizes the illness as a holistic process, it is important to begin to construct an image of healthy ideals that will replace and heal the disease-producing ones. This circle is constructed like the first one, but contains within it a central ideal to concentrate on. This central ideal then needs to be used as a focus for healing.

The use of the Illness Circle to define the process of an illness needs to include the strengths of the individual. What is healthy and right with an individual is just as important in healing as what is unhealthy. The unique way this person approaches his or her life is extremely important in defining an illness and seeking a healing solution. Each sick person should be considered an entire universe unto themselves, with their own unique strengths and weaknesses that can help or diminish the healing process. The unique attributes of this individual–whether courage, imagination, humility, curiosity, intelligence or whatever–are extremely important because they

ILLNESS/PROBLEM AS A PROCESS

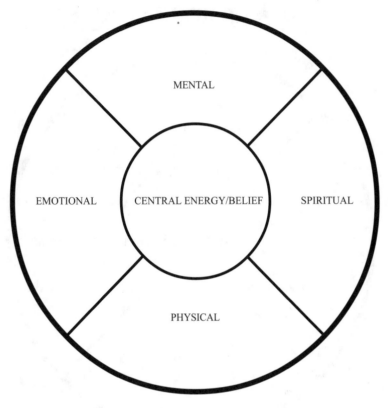

Fig. 2

Directions for the Illness Circle:

Begin in the lower quadrant of the physical listing your specific physical symptoms (not just the name of your illness). Then ask what function of the body is involved. Next ask what these symptoms symbolize in your mental, emotional, and spiritual life. Can you express this in a cliche of the body? (For instance, "I can't stomach this"if it is a stomach problem). Next look at what chakra or energy center is involved and what its issues are. Also note what the predominant energy (masculine or feminine energy) is. For instance, if the issue is in the heart chakra or in the chest-breast area where love is the dominant issue, ask yourself where have you had problems with not giving or receiving love or joy and how you can bring in more feminine energy to balance this.

HOLISTIC HEALTH IDEALS

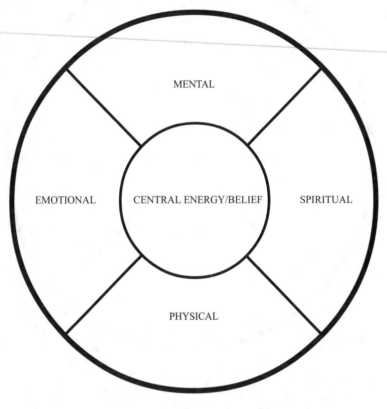

Fig. 3

Directions for the Ideals Circle: Begin by asking, what would balance or heal what is in your illness circle, not just be its opposite. Be as honest as possible in considering what the antidote or fulcrum issue would be that would balance the constricting beliefs—emotions of your physical symptoms. For instance, if your illness is heart disease, consider how you express or suppress your anger. Is this honest and appropriate? Does this interfere with your ability to love?

can be used in making the changes necessary to transform the disease processes.

The process for completing the Illness Circle is to write down the specific symptoms of your illness–what it is and does rather than merely its name. Then ask the following questions, focusing first on the specific symptoms of an illness: "What does the afflicted part of the body do? Is there a cliche that represents it?" Locate the troubled area on *Figure 1* and then ask what the central issue of the area or organ is. For example, if the heart is involved you need to ask yourself, "Do I love myself? Am I 'hard-hearted' to myself or others?" Then ask, "How are these specific physical symptoms symbolic or expressive of what is happening in the mental, emotional and spiritual aspects of my life."

It is recommended that you work on the completion of both circles first in a lightly relaxed state, and then in a deeply relaxed state with soothing music to obtain images of the illness and a healing symbol that can then be used in visualization of your healing. New insights are arrived at through deeper work with the subconscious than are usually possible otherwise. The central energy or belief behind an illness is important because this energy can be used in a practical way. Once the central energy or belief behind an illness is identified, you can begin to recognize the behavior and beliefs that are disease-producing and take practical, immediate action to change them.

Recognizing negative behavior can be done by recording how often and under what circumstances a specific personality pattern occurs, for example, how often one feels hostile to others. Through recognizing, you can make an evaluation of how it occurs and act to change it. If the central energy is that of feeling guilty and not taking enough time for yourself, you can record how and when this occurs and change your behavior in those situations. This graphic description of an illness in terms of its emotional, mental and physical components helps you see how you are responsible for creating the sickness in question. This process can be an encouraging one if you are honest and willing to take responsibility for creating any illness.

What often makes us ill is our choice to not think or feel deeply enough and instead to function from the patterns of the past in our negative egos. To remove these old patterns, we can, through the use of the will, set new ideals and, in more relaxed states, focus on what we want to build in our lives, reprogramming our subconscious minds. There is a great freedom and inspiration in the awareness that we can take control of a disease process and, by changing the underlying conflicts, become well.

To increase awareness of any particular disease process, it is important to identify the characteristic belief structure and associated emotions typical of the illness, as well as the unique ways each sick individual expresses these attitudes. For example, the specific disease-producing attitudes among people suffering from coronary heart disease are usually tendencies to hostility, time urgency, self destruction, hyperaggressiveness and status insecurity. This general information concerning Type A personalities then needs to be individualized to describe how you, as a unique individual with coronary heart disease, express these attitudes.

After you know the message of an illness, the *sixth* and final step in getting well is to pick a regimen of such things as visualization, diet, acupuncture, homeopathy, and medication, which you then follow to return to health. To suspend the process of an illness it is necessary to replace the central energy of an illness with a more healthy one.

Recently, I was diagnosed as having a mild case of hypothyroidism, with a goiter. Although I did not have the usual symptoms of this illness, the doctor prescribed an artificial thyroid substitute called Synthroid. The doctor told me hypothyroidism was a genetic disease that would progressively get worse.

I reasoned that substituting Synthroid for thyroid would lead my body to think it was producing enough thyroid when it was not, which would cause my thyroid gland to put out less and less thyroid, making me more dependent on Synthroid and thus fulfilling the doctor's prognosis. Instead, I used a regular program of visualization, meditation and herbs. The central energy behind my low thyroid functioning was a confusion of my will. The area of conflict was in allowing myself to express things freely, without struggle or fear of disapproval from others. I began to use my will more skillfully by relaxing and asking my body to help me achieve what was needed. When I did not struggle so much or depend so greatly on the approval of others, my confusion left, my goiter gradually got smaller, and my thyroid levels returned to within a normal range.

Using Holistic Principles in Healing

This process of both visualizing and using language that speaks of an illness as one process follows the principles of holistic medicine in a practical way. These principles are as follows:

(1) The individual person exists on many levels. These include the physical, the emotional, the mental and the spiritual, all of which are equally important in achieving health. None is "more real" than another. All must be taken into account to have a balanced life.

(2) The sick individual has self healing repair systems, and they must be regarded as crucial in the prevention and cure of disease.

(3) The patient must be actively and knowledgeably involved in his own treatment and in designing a program to work toward health.

(4) Each person is a unique individual and must be met and responded to as such. (LeShan, 1986)

This holistic approach not only honors the individuality of each sick person, but also the spiritual life of that person. This dimension of life, although overlooked or diminished in importance in scientific circles, often is a key element in the healing process. By spirituality I do not mean that one is religious; I mean that one has a living, breathing relationship with the spiritual elements of life and feels connected with life within and without. This attitude may be part of one's religion, but is not exclusively a religious attitude.

The Process of Healing a Gastrointestinal Illness

One central dysfunctional energy of an illness can be the belief, "I am here to please others, so I can earn the love I need." This belief was held by a woman I counseled named Sarah, who had numerous physical problems including ulcers, gastric upset and allergies. To become healthy, Sarah had to give up this pattern underlying her gastrointestinal problems. There were a number of things in Sarah's life that she could not stomach. These were issues she had been unable to process and release.

One of the functions of the digestive system is the processing of food. When we have emotions that are unexpressed, suppressed and unprocessed, often we have problems with the gastrointestinal system of our bodies. Until we can process and release these emotions, they eat upon us. Sarah had many angry feelings toward her mother, who lived nearby and would interfere in Sarah's family life. Sarah reacted like a victim and a helpless child when she was around her mother. Her mother likewise played the role of the martyred, unappreciated, misunderstood caretaker, and took no responsibility for her destructive influence on her daughter's life.

The main feeling Sarah held toward her mother was that of resentment. My work with Sarah began with releasing the destructive ties that held her to her mother. This was done using music and imagery to visualize where the ties were to her mother upon her body and to cut these ties with the help of inner guidance and a special pair of magical scissors. This visualization can be repeated several times until there is a feeling of release and freedom. This exercise had dramatic results; Sarah immediately began to act on her new sense of freedom by expressing her new sense of power within her family.

The central goal and ideal of our therapy was for Sarah to gain self esteem from inner validation and to learn to express her feelings honestly and appropriately. In order to release the resentment and hostility that Sarah felt toward her parents, it was necessary to deal with the hurt child within. This child wanted nothing more than to be loved and would not grow until she received this love. As long as the hurt child dominated Sarah's life, she could be easily manipulated by her mother and other people who withheld love from her.

To heal the hurt child within Sarah, we had to return to those times in her childhood when that child felt helpless, abused and alone. Sarah was the child of an alcoholic father who was emotionally and physically abusive of her, and of a mother who martyred herself by supporting such a man. There were many times in childhood that Sarah was left alone with her father and felt frightened and helpless. Her mother, instead of protecting her, placed her in the position of being his caretaker. Using Guided Imagery and Music, we together returned to those places in her childhood where Sarah felt hurt and overwhelmed. We also brought with us a loving father and guide. This father protected the child within her and allowed her to express the anger she was still feeling. The child within who still needs love and protection can be given this. When this need was fulfilled, Sarah's adult self was free to grow without interference from her inner child.

The results of healing the hurt child within were dramatic for Sarah. Instead of being the helpless victim within her family, she began to make the changes that she knew needed to be made. Her relationship with her mother changed dramatically. Since Sarah would no longer play the victim to her mother's martyrdom, her mother stopped playing the martyr and began showing her more affection and respect. She also stopped interfering so much in Sarah's family affairs, and life was much more peaceful among them. Instead of playing the role of the helpless child or victim, Sarah began to display and feel a new sense of self-esteem.

Using Guided Imagery and Music, Sarah searched within herself and found a book containing her beliefs about her self-esteem. Those beliefs that were no longer constructive were destroyed and other more positive ones were written there instead. In the room of emotion, Sarah faced the fears in her life with the help of a gentle inner guide who protected her. Together we explored the beliefs that had allowed her to fall into a pattern of victimhood and compliance to the will of others. Sarah replaced these with more constructive beliefs that allowed her to grow.

Sarah began practicing the ideals of self-love, honesty and responsibility, which built her self-esteem. Many of the strengths and abilities she had previously suppressed or denied found new expression. The deep resentments Sarah held toward her mother gradually changed to more loving feelings as she began taking responsibility for rebuilding her family life in a more positive way. Sarah's physical problems gradually improved as she gained more and more inner balance and control of her life. It is quite probable that the large number of people who suffer from ulcers and gastrointestinal problems could be dramatically helped if holistic counseling were regularly available to them.

It is important in healing to recognize and take responsibility for an underlying conflict so that it can be replaced by more healthy patterns; more healthy patterns can be developed alone or through counseling. Arthritis, for instance, is in many ways an impulse to reach for freedom and a suppression of that urge. Behind the arthritic posture that inhibits feelings is the need to express anger and affection. Understanding what is behind arthritis, however, needs to be accompanied by emotional involvement. Without emotional involvement in the healing process, no change in the physical body can be permanently healing.

My Healing Practice Using Imagery, Music and Relaxation

In my practice as a holistic therapist, I use a technique called Guided Imagery and Music, in which a person experiences specially selected (mostly new age and classical) music in a relaxed state of body and mind. The purpose of this is to evoke emotions, images and messages from the deep inner mind for purposes of healing, growth and creativity. I learned this method through the Institute of Consciousness and Music, founded by Helen Bonny, and use it in a focused, intuitive way, directed towards goals that have been agreed upon with the person I am counseling. These goals often include healing some particular illness-producing process.

Over the years, I have come to trust my intuition to know just what to do and where to go to accomplish holistic healing needs. My main goal is to help the individual I am counseling come to a spontaneous perception of his or her illness that is more than a release of repressed or denied feelings and more than understanding. It is my goal to assist the person I am counseling in building an honest perception of the conflict behind an illness. This perception is one in which he or she perceives the larger picture and allows intuitive meanings and emotional understandings to come.

Such an overview surpasses any words, thoughts, imagery or feelings. This broad perception is an expansive feminine energy–pure knowledge that comes from using the co-creative feminine energy of the higher consciousness within both men and women. This perception, however, grows out of a balance in which both thought and feeling work together to create understanding and meaning. In my practice, I balance the powerful feminine energies of feeling, imaging and perception with the equally powerful masculine energies of seeking understanding and meaning. The use of the two healing circles is a masculine form that helps bring together all the factors that are important to an illness and to see how these interact with each other.

Music is valuable in the healing of illness because illness is caused mainly by denied or repressed emotions. Music is an extremely effective tool because it helps you evoke the powerful feminine energies of feeling and imagination. As you open to your ability to imagine and then to feel, you can cleanse denied or repressed emotions such as anger and hurt that are the basis of an illness. Music is the greatest natural truth serum there is; it invites emotional honesty, and through this, healing. Healing occurs for you when you are freed of the constraint, alienation, disorder and failure that illness often represents.

Music and relaxation are tools that help you confront the conflicts underlying an illness. A holistic evaluation of an illness process helps those I counsel see clearly what their specific illness represents and how it can be healed. There are books that give specific meanings for various illnesses; these are helpful but cannot replace the deep intuitive knowledge that comes when you perceive the conflicts behind your specific illness. When you recognize, own, forgive and then replace a destructive pattern with a constructive one, healing has begun to take place.

Drawings and Healing

Another helpful way to get a broad perspective on an illness is through drawing. You may wish to draw a picture of your illness, your immune system, your treatment and its healing. This will give both you and your therapist insight as to how you feel about your illness and its healing. For instance, a woman who wished to heal a fibroid she had in her uterus drew a large black X over the genital area of her body which indicated to us both that there were still conflicts concerning her sexuality. Sometimes I also ask the ill individual to picture his life as a play and then to draw a picture of the principal characters in both his internal life-play and his outer one. To draw the outer life play, I ask him to represent the principal people in his life by circles for women and triangles for men, and to place the principal player first in the middle of the page and the other players around him.

When this configuration is completed, I ask if the picture suggests a central theme to him. If, for instance, he places the circle that represents himself inside the triangle that represents his wife, what theme does this configuration suggest? Where these figures are placed in relationship to one another helps him see clearly the themes and patterns of power in his life.

This outer drawing is then supplemented by an inner drawing of the child, adolescent, parental, higher consciousness and ego parts of the inner self which can be drawn in any color or shape they appear. By doing such an exercise, a broad perspective can be obtained in a short time as to the relative power and influence of the inner parts of the self.

In one such drawing, Irene, who had a chronic skin condition, drew the negative ego and the critical parent parts of herself as large, dark figures superimposed on each other, and her higher consciousness as small, undeveloped and unimportant. Irene identified with the negative-ego/critical-parent part of the self and felt that it was her life. This drawing helped her take the next step suggested by the image, writing out the beliefs that she held which were similar to those of her parents. This list was then rewritten and, when she was ready, burned and replaced by one that was much more nurturing and accepting of herself and others. Irene blamed her father, husband and co-workers for the failures in her life and felt self-righteous and self-important. She had a dream in which she blamed her father for having lost and ruined her car. This dream seemed to be pointing out to her how she blamed others, especially men, for her unhappiness. Her payoff of self-importance was reflected by a husband who saw her as a self-centered, self-important person. He responded by staying away from her and becoming absorbed in other activities such as playing tennis or watching TV.

Another individual drew the adolescent part of herself as red and dark, holding the child part of herself which was pink, prominent and vulnerable within her inner image. This gave us a clue that these parts of the self were important at that time–that the feelings and thoughts behind those images needed to be addressed. By creating a drawing of the inner and outer scenes, it is easier to be objective about them and to come to a decision about what needs to be healed.

To change, it is also important that ill individuals see what payoffs and poisons are indicated by their illness and then determine whether they are willing to make the choices necessary to give them up. Payoffs and poisons such as blame, self-pity, avoidance and self-importance need to be released if one is to become well physically, emotionally and spiritually.

When I am working with someone, I always follow the principle of addressing the issue that is most emotionally troubling to that person at the time. It is never enough, however, to be a conduit for the release of negative emotions. All ill individuals benefit temporarily from such a release, but this release needs to be accompanied by an atmosphere in which the sick person gains a perspective and a sense of authority over his or her life. Not only does such a perspective give one an opportunity to release repressed or denied emotions, but it also provides a chance to create more constructive patterns. This perspective comes from both thinking and feeling. Feeling helps stimulate thought, and thought helps deepen feeling; both are important in healing.

Relaxation

For relaxation, I teach others to use *receptive will* as I learned to use it in healing myself of hypothyroidism. The passive will is not something most people learn in life; it goes against our cultural training. Our culture teaches us that to get what we want we have to actively strive for it, but this does not work with our bodies. The more you try to force your body to fall asleep, for instance, the more wide awake you will become. It is only when you use the receptive will and let your body become more and more relaxed that it actually does what is wanted–whether you are trying to fall asleep or to heal yourself. When you are relaxed, your body and mind are receptive to what you wish to take place in them.

The process of self-healing I use begins with allowing yourself to relax in whatever way is most comfortable to you. There are many ways to relax, including counting your breaths, focusing on a mantra or counting up or down. If you are completely new at this process of relaxation, I suggest you begin by speaking gently and lovingly to the various parts of your body, beginning with either your head or your feet, and suggesting to them that they relax. Once you have learned to relax in whatever way is most effective for you, you can begin to use imagery in a focused, purposeful and skillful way to heal yourself.

Healing Myself of Hypothyroidism

In healing myself of a hypothyroid condition, I became aware that the central energy of my illness was a confusion of my will that created an inability to express myself effectively. I did not have my right-creative brain in cooperation with my critical, analytic brain. Using the Illness and Wellness circles, I did a holistic assessment of the meaning of my hypothyroid condition with the goiter at my throat. My thought processes were, "What I say does not matter, is not important, or I do not know enough." This was contrary to my impulse to speak from my insights and experiences. I was inspired to speak, yet remained silent for fear of reprisal and of exposing myself to abuse. This fear of speaking led to anger and frustration at not being heard or understood and to a stagnation of the will since I was stuck in a nonproductive mode. The confusion of my will came from fear. I had to begin to care less about the approval of others, and to act and speak with integrity.

The most important factor in my recovery was to not wait for others to give me permission to speak, but to give myself permission to express what I knew to be truth. To heal, I had to say "No" to the critical negative part of myself that devalued what I said or did. The goiter at my throat was a nonmalignant growth that built up scar tissue on my thyroid gland, the result of an autoimmune disease in which my body was attacking itself. My mind was telling my thyroid gland to produce more thyroid because that gland was somehow malfunctioning. My role was to become more active, more assertive and more self-assured in my verbal acts. I could not wait for others to approve of the inspirations and creative thoughts that came into my mind. I was already a poet and writer, but my body was telling me that an even higher and more elegant, balanced level of creativity was possible for me. My ideal for myself was the responsibility, permission and support to speak freely.

When I would not express the words I was compelled to express, my body spoke for me by growing where I should have grown. This conflict was a reoccurrence of one I had as an adolescent that manifested a similar symptom, also at the throat. When I was sixteen years old I developed a large benign cyst that would swell and fill with a pussy substance, although drained at numerous times. This cyst finally had to be removed surgically. I was shy as an adolescent, but was also an intelligent young person who had much to say. The school system rewarded my studious shyness and at the same time punished it. I often suppressed my desire to speak, to be a good student and to belong. This conflict again returned in middle age when I developed hypothyroidism.

The feelings that were asociated with the thought that what I said did not matter were fear, confusion, self-pity, anger, disappointment and doubt. This attitude was one in which I expected what I had to say would not be heard, or would be ignored or invalidated by others. My hypothyroidism was a mild form of autoimmune disease, a disease of defenseless, suppressed people. I recognized that, like other autoimmune diseases, when I would not defend myself in my frustration and anger, when I would not speak up and express myself regardless of others' reactions, my body would defend me. It is significant that hypothyroidism is predominantly a women's disease. It affects women over age forty 14 times more often than men, but can occur at any age. I recognized that women were more likely to feel ignored, put down and consequently feel that what they had to say was useless.

Women are often reluctant to speak up for themselves and others, and to speak their truth when it is opposed to the consensus reality. I fully recognized that many of my ideas were new and contrary to those of the common opinion. I had to recognize that I could not serve two masters. I had to quit trying to get approval from those whose opinions differed; I had to speak my truth.

Besides allowing myself to speak freely, I began expecting my goiter and hypothyroidism to be gone. I regularly visualized it growing smaller and burning away with the blue-orange flame of free speech. I started being more responsible and assertive in my writing and speaking, reflecting an integrity to my experience. I faced situations of fear and overcame this fear to say what needed to be said. I spoke out against logging a local county park and wrote more and better prose and poetry. I also became a more balanced, effective counselor.

It is significant that the goiter at my throat was more swollen on my left side than on my right. This indicated to me that I was more conflicted in expressing feelings, imaginations, and tendernesses, from my feminine side. These were things I was most talented in expressing, but qualities my culture devalued. It was necessary for me to fully value this feminine energy before I could teach others of its value. In one year, the thyroid level of my blood had returned to normal and my TSH blood level had lowered, indicating my brain had stopped attacking my throat to stimulate growth. As I became more responsible in my expression, the goiter at my throat gradually diminished until it was gone. The essence of my healing was to learn to nurture and express myself without conflict, in more efficient ways. This meant I had to unplug a "negative, critical ego" that shut me up, controlled, sickened and defeated me. My body healed itself once the conflict was gone.

Color and Healing

I find that colors are some of the most powerful images you can use; like sound, they have a frequency and vibration that the mind responds to directly. To imagine color requires changes in the brain which activate and heal nerves and glandular activities within the body and brain. Red, green and blue are the primary healing colors for the body. As a general rule, use green for those cells having to do with building, such as bones, heart, blood and reproductive organs. Use red for those cells having to do with fueling the body, such as lungs, intestines, kidneys, liver, connecting tissues, problems of low energy, and when under- or overweight. Blue is the color to use for problems related to the brain and the nervous system.

Each individual should always decide on the color that is most healing for him- or herself. One woman with a chronic itch on her legs was able to cure this condition within a week by visualizing herself swimming in a turquoise bay of water like a dolphin for fifteen minutes each night before she went to bed. Unfortunately, the itch returned later because she had not dealt with the underlying problem that it symbolized. Violet is a particularly effective color to use with cancerous tumors because this color contains both the power of blue and red. The blue acts on the nervous system that is active in the formation of cancer, and the red acts to strengthen the immune system that fights cancerous tumors.

Transformation

A healing meditation centers the subconscious on some particular problem or symptom and allows the superconscious to bring us messages and images of healing. Music appropriate for meditation may be quieter classical music such as Debussy's *"Afternoon of the Faun"* or Holsts' *"Venus from the Planets,"* or various selections from the works of Vaughn Williams such as *"Fantasia on Greensleeves."* I also recommend adaptions of classical music to a slower tempo such as Daniel Kobialka's extended version of *"Ode to Joy"* by Beethoven on the tape *Sunspace.*

After meditation, take time to write about or draw your experience. Describe the image of your symptom or problem in detail and then the image of your healing. As you evaluate your experience, maintain the nonjudgemental attitude of a discoverer and consider your problem from a broad perspective. Evaluate whether what you learned from this experience is helpful. Record your insights and decide how you can act upon them. Focus particularly on the healing image as a symbolic representation that can help you form a healing ideal. Ask yourself what qualities the healing image represents.

When you understand the qualities of the image, use them in setting your healing ideals and completing your Wellness Circle (*Figure 3*). This healing ideal will be the focus necessary for meeting the needs causing your symptom. Now that you have a healing ideal set, begin to use it in practical ways. If your ideal is freedom to express anger (a common problem for arthritics), begin to express your anger in meditation. Gradually increase this expression to more fearful, threatening situations.

The Healing of Candidiasis

A woman named Cecillia visualized her illness as a heavy metal bell without a ringer inside. For the image of her healing she saw a crystal bell that made a lovely sound. When we explored the meaning of her imagery further, we learned more about what these symbols represented. Cecillia had candidiasis (candida) and food allergies that limited her diet. Even with a restricted diet and medication she felt ill. Her imagery pointed to a refusal to express the intensity of her feelings. As a child, Cecillia had been programmed by her father to become tough, hard and emotionless in order to survive in an unfriendly world.

To heal this emotional blockage, she reeducated the child within her by going back to important childhood memories in which she had been told not to feel. Cecillia relived these incidents and allowed the child within to feel and express all her anger and hurt. She encouraged her inner child to feel that it was safe to express her feelings.

Cecillia also rehearsed a confrontation with her husband in which she expressed her feelings and needs despite her fears. It had been particularly difficult to express her feelings to her husband because she projected the tough, defensive way she used to act with her father onto him. Cecillia's health improved dramatically as she allowed her feelings to be expressed more freely. She found a crystal bell and kept this near her to remind herself that her health lay in the beauty of her clear emotional expression. Images from the subconscious often contain an emotional and spiritual component that is not understood by intellect alone; they speak to our higher consciousness that transcends logic and reason.

Processing and Programming to Heal

In our society, we fear many diseases and think we cannot control them because we see only the surface, the physical reality that created them. We think, for instance, that we are betrayed by an illness such as cancer or heart disease, and therefore feel betrayed by the Creator. We do not see the underlying sequence of events and feelings that led up to the creation of that particular illness. The person with a life threatening illness such as cancer was definitely not in harmony before he or she became ill. Despite a superficial semblance of health, much conflict is hidden.

People with cancer, for instance, are not betrayed by the Creator. They are betrayed by the dark side of themselves they deny which is killing them–their negative egos. George, who was dying of a brain tumor, had a critical parental self that worked with his negative ego to suppress the rage he felt. George was a perfectionist and was angry at himself for his failure. He was angry at himself for having made mistakes, and not pleasing others.

From childhood on, George believed society's promises that said to not think or feel, just do and you will succeed. George was fired from a prestigious job, because he made the mistake of getting injured. George denied and refused to face his rage and self-pity. This conflict found expression in an inoperable brain tumor that eventually killed him. To heal himself, George needed to face his rage and perfectionism and learn to trust himself. *To process this illness, he would have had to recognize, own, forgive and change the beliefs and choices behind the tumor.* George would have had to recognize the circumstances of his life did not create his conflict. His conflict was caused by the negativity within himself which he shoved down and refused to face. To heal, George needed to forgive himself for believing that if he was perfect, he would always succeed. He had to allow himself to make mistakes and be forgiven.

Chapter Four

Attitudes That Heal,
Attitudes That Destroy

Our attitudes depend upon our beliefs; they are the coloration or hue that our beliefs produce. We can take control of and heal our illnesses by identifying and changing those beliefs and their accompanying attitudes from which an illness grew. High blood pressure, for instance, represents an attitude of fear and a belief in an unfriendly world. If you change your belief that this is a fearful world, your defensive attitude also changes, and your blood pressure decreases. Your mental attitude can be the pivotal point where an illness overcomes you or causes you to grow. The attitudes that heal are those of trust in yourself and your physician or healer, responsibility, hope, gratitude, and a will to live. Attitudes that destroy are those of self-pity, depression, helplessness, blame and defeatism. Your healing or destructive attitude represents a choice that is made, whether consciously or unconsciously.

Responsibility

Your role in developing an illness leads eventually to the question of responsibility. Mostly we deny responsibility; after all, who *wants* to be ill? In the literature concerning the psychological factors related to illness, the concept of responsibility is often overlooked or misinterpreted. The literature on psychosomatic illness usually limits the concept of responsibility to the choice of how one reacts to stress, either in a positive or negative way. To answer the underlying causes of an illness, responsibility must be seen in its broadest sense and tied to power.

Without responsibility, you are powerless. Responsibility is the key to not only power, but to the result of power, which is freedom. In our culture we have focused only upon the negative side of responsibility, its burdens, without seeing the positive side that creates our health.

Illness is something that begins from within us and therefore can be healed by changing our ideas and attitudes. When we hold a belief that our bodies are machines that break down, over which we have no control, we naturally look to available outside forces to heal us and to battle the hostile substances that have gained entry. When we loose faith in our ability to control our bodies, we believe we are insecure and easily betrayed both by our bodies and our environment; this attitude adds to the conflict of insecurity that promotes disease. To refute this destructive attitude, the following question needs to be explored: Why is it that some people who are exposed to the same viruses, germs or environmental pollutants do not become ill while others do?

The idea that some illnesses are psychosomatic, such as peptic ulcer, colitis, and bronchial asthma, while others are not has been challenged by the holistic health movement, which assumes all illnesses are related to mental and emotional states. There is no reality that is outside the boundary of our beliefs and attitudes. If you believe that the immune system and healing power of your body and mind is stronger and more powerful than any illness, then once internal conflict is healed, illness can be overcome.

The popular attitude is that the center of healing is the responsibility of the physician, when really it is always within the patient. A patient's ability (or lack of ability) to choose to exercise the full range of positive emotions, and to demonstrate confidence, a will to live, hope, love, purpose and joyousness, determine the outcome of an illness. It is important to reach for an attitude in which you have self-regulation over your body and its functions, not by restrictive control, but by the choice of beliefs and their related emotions that are consistent with peacefulness and happiness. This can be done by recognizing that there are other more positive alternatives to an illness, than the way of conflict that illness symbolizes.

Self-regulation of your body is possible only if you see that your body is your creation. Your body is an intensely energized form which reflects back to you your emotions and thoughts over the years. If your body is strong and healthy, so have been your thoughts and feelings. It is true that you are much more than your body, but at the same time your body expresses you fully; its degree of health and aliveness reflects your own. The feedback system of your body helps you be honest and responsible for conflicts you need to face and resolve.

Healing requires that the patient be provided with alternative modes of behavior. The emphasis on responsibility for healing in holistic medicine is an antidote to the defeatism, negativity and fear that often follows the feeling of being victimized by an illness. If you think of your body as a machine that will eventually break down and wear out, over which you have little or no control, you are in submission to it, and to the mechanic (your doctor) who knows more than you do about how to fix it. If you think of your body as a self generating system and as yourself as your own healer, you then are able to take control of your healing and life.

One of the most destructive patterns of behavior is self-pity, which comes often in the initial stage of an illness when a patient feels "victimized" by an illness. While self-pity is something no one in our society likes to admit, at the same time it is an attitude that is supported by our educational system and culture. Self-pity is an underlying cause of many illnesses because it numbs your feelings; it is also a consequence of following the traditional attitudes toward illness.

The most common roles in our society that are based upon self-pity and not taking responsibility are the overworked martyr, the victim, the perfectionistic struggler, and the suffering rescuer. All of these roles set the player up for illness. Victims and martyrs use the payoffs of self-pity and importance to control and manipulate others.

Mrs. Brown was chronically ill and used that to demand attention from her grown-up children. When this attention was not given, her children were accused of not loving her and were threatened with disinheritance. On one occasion, Mrs. Brown summoned her daughter Caroline to the hospital in the middle of the night. Caroline refused to go because she felt this was only another way for her mother to manipulate her. Mrs. Brown then accused Caroline of lack of love. Instead of obtaining the love, respect and attention she desperately desired, Mrs. Brown's manipulations merely served to alienate her family from her. Mrs. Brown's family felt sorry for her, and thought of her as an annoying person who had to be tolerated.

Self-pity can be reinforced or elicited by the attitudes of those around us. It is very destructive to seriously ill people for others to take an attitude of pity, because it undermines their own sense of dignity and responsibility and their confidence in their healing power. If the people around those who are sick do not think they have any chance to recover, it is difficult for the sick person to remain positive. Regardless of predictions of the medical profession to the contrary, miracles of healing can occur if we are open to them.

Self Regulation

I have learned from my experience and work that our vital signs, such as blood pressure and pulse, are much more subject to our regulation and to the influence of our thoughts and feeling than most of us realize.

Chapter 4   Attitudes That Heal, Attitudes That Destroy

Barbara came to me to help her reduce her high blood pressure. When Barbara was a young women, she had one of her breasts removed after being told it was cancerous. Later, she was told that there was a mistake and her breast had not been cancerous at all. When Barbara reached 65, her old age script took effect and her blood pressure became elevated. It was not unreasonable for Barbara to fear doctors who had betrayed her and her body. Treatment of her high blood pressure had as much to do with regaining a sense of trust in her ability to self-regulate her blood pressure and to trust herself as she grew older as it had to do with managing her fear. Her fear was related to the maltreatment she had received from doctors whom she had trusted and had allowed to misuse their authority.

High blood pressure medications are essential for many people, yet for many others high blood pressure medications have side effects that are harmful; each person should explore all the options keeping in mind that situational reactions such as fear and anger (especially to medical personnel) can have much to do with an increase in blood pressure.

The important lesson for me was learning to trust that I could regulate my body, mind and emotions. I learned that by simple relaxation techniques such as deep breathing and talking to my body and asking it to feel "rest," I can lower my blood pressure and control my fear and anger. Fear is a warning sign that is useful when it alerts you to the danger that is justified in many medical settings. This fear however need not betray you, nor do you need fear medical personnel who try to take your power away. The real issue may be to learn to handle your fear of authority by giving yourself dominion or authority over your body. Some medical personnel are trustworthy and some are not; it is up to you to keep your power and to trust yourself, including your feelings to tell you the difference. My choice is to trust myself and my body.

It is common for doctors to frighten people, especially women, by suggesting that "their way" to deal with an illness or problem is the only way. Any medical person who uses scare tactics such as "do it my way or die" is misusing his or her power. This misuse contributes to conflicted attitudes of fear and insecurity that underlie many illnesses. The best way to deal with such scare tactics is the one I recommend, "Pay your bill as you leave the office, wipe your feet, say goodbye, and do not look back." There are many wise physicians who are sensitive, caring people who will neither intimidate you, nor rob you of your own healing power and dignity.

Self-regulation is confidence in your ability to depend upon your positive ego functioning so you can survive or cope with your outer reality, including your body. One way to build your confidence in your body is to build its components, which are trust, hope, humility and courage. As a self confident person, you approach an illness with trust in your body, your emotions, intelligence, intuition and inner guidance. Humility is not a groveling attitude or a "less than others" posture, but the willingness to look at each experience in a new way, no matter how many times others have encountered it before. The person who has cancer, for instance, needs humility and courage to see that his cancer is unlike any other he has ever read about or heard of. Without hope or courage, you have no self-confidence. Hope, trust, humility and courage, will help you become self-confident to heal yourself of any illness.

Trusting Your Body

Your body is an expression of the multidimensional reality of what you are. You are much more than your body. You can view your body as a vehicle, or as a friend that can help you reach higher states of awareness. It can be seen as a trusted teacher–a two-way monitor of the reality inside and outside yourself. Illness represents places of conflict where a deeper awareness is blocked. You can heal this blockage by reconnecting the dimensions of your awareness, reconnecting your body, mind and spirit.

Our society has made the mistake of thinking of the body as a machine that wears out in time, but this does not have to be. You have intelligent regenerative cells, responsive to your deficiencies. A spiritual or emotional deficiency is just as deadly as a lack of important vitamins and minerals, because your cells respond to it. For instance, people who live alone (particularly divorced men) are more likely to become ill and die at an early age. When you lack love, compassion and caring for yourself and others, your body automatically responds (with illness) to get the imbalance corrected.

Illness is meant to be a feedback mechanism to alert us to get back on the path of our own spontaneous fulfillment, happiness and integrity. In this capacity, it can be considered a friend whose illness messages are either of two kinds, those that ask for help or those that offer it. Your body's messages can be seen as the natural response from a friend to a friend. One part of your multidimensional self in illness is crying for compassion and attention from another part. A diseased liver, for instance, is asking for help to release stored feelings of anger. A sore muscle may be offering help by saying, "You have overstretched your endurance for exercise. You need rest."

We ignore minor discomforts such as sore muscles or slight pains, and even major illnesses, because of our massive distrust of our bodies. Our fear of what these symptoms mean prevents us from being intimate with, trusting of, and in touch with our bodies. Much of our fear comes because we do not think we can heal our bodies. To do so, we need to seek out the frustrated desire, impulse, or conflict that is present and resolve it. Deepak Chopra tells of one of his patients, a woman in great pain from bone cancer. Immediately after she saw she was "weary to the bone" from her destructive marriage, and she had made the decision to divorce her husband, the pain from her bone cancer disappeared.

Illness and imbalance come when the body experiences strain pressure and discomfort inside and out; this strain may be a spiritual lack of love or compassion–an emptiness of the heart. To correct the imbalance among body, mind and spirit, it is first necessary to come to an awareness of where in your body the discomfort is. This is done by admitting to the mental, emotional and physical pain rather than denying it or "stuffing" it away in your body. This first step of expressing where it hurts helps to prevent illness. By paying attention to your body and feeling what is happening to it–any and all reactions–you begin to reconnect. To do this, sit comfortably on a chair or couch. Notice your body sensations. Do you feel your feet on the floor? Do you feel the contact of your arms on whatever is supporting them? Particularly, do you feel symptoms such as tightness in your neck, a twinge of pain in your muscles, or discomfort in your shoulders? Ask then what these symptoms represent. Allow your attention to go where it needs to go to do this.

Once while doing this exercise, I became aware of a soreness and heaviness in my shoulders. My higher consciousness alerted me to the awareness that I had taken on too much care for others and not enough for myself. I needed to lighten up and not be so serious. A white silk cloak was placed upon my shoulders to remind me I did not need to struggle so much to be a creative and loving person.

The important lesson for me is to trust that I can regulate my body, mind and emotions. Pain in my body can be seen as a friendly signal that there is a lack of comfort or a conflict somewhere in my life that I need to resolve. I have learned that simple relaxation techniques such as deep breathing and asking my body to feel "rest" lower my blood pressure. My blood pressure rises when I feel panic, fear or anger. Fear is a warning sign that is useful when it alerts you to real danger, and it is up to you to then take the time to reflect upon what you fear and resolve it.

The Issue of Trust and Medical Care

The question of whether your health provider is trustworthy is often a life or death one. In one recent year more people died from having taken prescription drugs that their doctors gave them than the combined number who died from either illicit drugs or AIDS.

82

(Lazaris tape, 1994) This is because their doctors gave them samples which were given to the doctors by salesmen or because the patients were not properly instructed about how they should take the medications, for example, with or without food.

It is wise to always be cautious concerning medical advice or prescriptions given. Always ask questions about the side effects of medications and the long-term effects a drug may have on your body. If you do not like what you learn, look into other alternative methods that are less likely to cause harm. Find out, for instance, what natural herbs or homeopathic remedies stimulate rather than interfere with the natural balance of your body. If your intuition tells you not to take a medication, do not, until you know enough to make a wise choice. If you cannot do the research yourself concerning a drug or treatment, find someone you trust who has done it to your satisfaction. Avoid taking drug company samples if these are in dosages not individualized to you, and be sure to ask under what conditions medications should be taken.

When faced with instances of careless and life-threatening medical care, we wonder whom we can trust. I do not personally research every health problem, treatment and medication. Instead, I allow others I trust to do some of it. Hormone replacement therapy during and after menopause is a good example. Menopause is an extremely complicated issue and a challenging time for women around my age. Instead of accepting the "total solution" of some doctors and drug companies that advocate hormone replacement therapy, it is important to do some independent study on the subject, or to examine the work of women who have done so. Although I disagree with many of Germaine Greer's ideas concerning women's power, she has sought to find the highest truth concerning menopause. Greer does not accept the common medical attitude that menopause is a hormone deficiency disease that can be treated only with hormone replacement therapy. In her book, *The Change, Women, Aging, and the Menopause,* Greer cautions that the progesterone usually taken with estrogen can undo the benefits that estrogen provides in relationship to heart disease. To take estrogen alone is considered dangerous because it is asociated with the growth of uterine and breast cancer.

Hormone replacement therapy also may prevent the establishment of a new and more natural pattern of estrogen secretion in menopausal women. If not interfered with, estrogen begins to be produced more from the stromal cells and the adrenals in menopausal women. When foreign estrogen dominates a woman's body, it may actually prevent the establishment of this new pattern and therefore later compromise her health and accelerate her aging.

Neither is it advisable to remain passive when you suffer debilitating symptoms at the time of menopause. Diet, exercise, herbs and homeopathic and naturopathic remedies are often curative. Dr. Gladys McGarey, associated with the A.R.E. Clinic in Phoenix, Arizona, often prescribes natural herbs and a trusty old Edgar Cayce remedy, atomodine, for relieving troublesome menopausal symptoms. When deciding whom I can trust, I first trust myself and then other health care providers who have demonstrated that they are worthy of my trust. This trust is not given on the basis of their authority, title or degrees, but on the basis of their actions. I give my trust to health care providers who have sought the highest truth available and have explored all possible alternatives concerning the treatment of a particular health problem. I do not trust those who have merely accepted without question the authority of other unreliable sources, such as drug companies which often are more interested in profits than in truth.

A Will to Live

A desire to live is necessary for good health. Psychology has not yet conceptualized a useful way of describing the desire to live. Freud theorized that there was an instinct to live and an instinct to die. Instead of considering the desire to live as an instinct beyond our conscious control, it is more accurate to think of it as a focused belief system which represents a conscious choice of a life that is fully lived.

Each of us has a death script that tells us how and when we will die. These scripts can be rewritten to allow us to live longer and fuller lives. Many of our death scripts are based upon a hopelessness and callousness that we take in from our mass media or family heritage. The hopelessness that triggers a death script is a choice. To choose hopelessness is to have a dullness of imagination that actively or passively rejects the real possibilities that lie dormant under even the most difficult of situations.

Your thoughts and feelings concerning how and when you will die are part of your death script. Death scripts are related to old age scripts, because old age is so intolerable for some people that they will not allow themselves to experience it. Since beliefs precede experience, what you believe concerning old age, you are likely to experience. If it is part of your family tradition to die at 65, if you expect to die at this time, you probably will. To find out what your death script is, ask yourself honestly, "When and under what conditions do I think I will die?" If you have, for instance, the death script that people who are weak and sick should die, when you become weak and sick you are likely to die.

One of the most harmful attitudes towards death is considering life as a competition in which death is the final failure. Death should not be considered a failure. If and when it is a conscious choice, death can be the ultimate healing. Certain important incidents, beliefs and attitudes may not be part of the medical record, but they may be of such importance that they can change the entire course of an illness. Events of striking force such as the birth or death of a loved one, the beginning or the end of your life's work, or the anniversary of the date that a mother or father died are important factors that can influence the will to live. These factors may be considered too unscientific, too unimportant to be noticed, yet these are the factors which can determine whether a person will live or die. In his book, *The Will to Live*, Dr. Hutschnecker tells many stories of how some important factor, such as a newly found love or a desire to live long enough to accomplish some important things, caused patients to miraculously recover from a life-threatening illness.

I agree with Hutschnecker that we choose our time of death, but disagree with him that this choice is instinctive. To call something instinctive is to imply that we have no choice in the matter. I believe we choose how and when we will die; this happens largely through our system of beliefs (our death script) and we have the power to choose new beliefs.

A neighbor of ours, George, died recently at a comparatively young age. He had often spoken of his desire to live at least as long as his father–who had died at 52. George had prepared in every way for his own death. Although he had survived a bypass operation, he seemed to sense that he would die soon. George had even told his wife that she would be better off financially if he died than if he were alive. The family had been building a new home, and when he spoke of this house, it was always in terms of it being for his wife and children, not for himself. Shortly after he turned 52, his heart condition became worse and he died during a heart operation.

The failure to find a reason to live is the unsolved problem that blocks the will to live for many cancer patients. In his research on the psychosocial reasons that predisposed a person to cancer, Lawrence LeShan discovered two important factors. These people had lost their reason for being, and they had inhibited their assertive expression of anger. The Type C-pattern people who are suscep-tible to cancer learn to deny and hold onto the negative part of themselves within their bodies where it cannot be seen by the world. This hidden part of themselves is so deep and scary that even they are unaware of its presence. By refusing to recognize, feel and express the presence of emotions such as anger, hurt and fear, these become negative. Without access to their feelings, life becomes flat, mediocre and desperate; they lose their real passions for life.

Their identity lies at the bottom of their hidden feelings. The complex of beliefs related to Type C behavior are these:

(1) It is useless to express my needs and assumptions.

(2) My needs or wants will not be met by my environment.

(3) If I express my real emotions, I will be rejected.

(4) My creative impulses are not all right if that does not meet with approval from those upon whom I depend.

To recover, cancer patients must change these beliefs to rediscover their uniqueness.

The world view of such patients can be corrected if they see that the solution lies within themselves, not in the outside world. In his work with cancer patients, LeShan found that "the will to live" has been tied to outer-directed concerns rather than a drive for self-realization. The neglect of their own inner development is strongly related to the weakness of their will to live. Since their energies are expressed in ways of life that give them little satisfaction, they have little energy left; this exhaustion of the will to live opens the door to disease. One of LeShan's patients, speaking of the past said, "If I looked ahead in life, there was nothing I could see unless I kidded myself."

Part of LeShan's role as a therapist is work with terminally ill cancer patients to reawaken the desire to live. LeShan explored the positive aspects of their lives with them—the interests that excited and compelled them to grow and live. For one woman named Lois this was a strong interest in anything that had to do with ballet. Lois's life again took on purpose when she began to research and write a book on the history of ballet in New York City.

LeShan wrote that the real theme of his book, *You Can Fight For Your Life*, was hope. "Amongst those stricken by the disease," he wrote, "the people most capable of recovery are the men and women who can discover a new wellspring of hope, whatever their past disappointments, and move on to a fresh sense of themselves, a true recognition of their needs and their worth as human beings."

Expectancy and Hope

Expectancy is essential to health. Without it, you live a life of frustration in which your dreams are never realized. Expectancy is necessary to the energies of trust, value, happiness and love. When your expectations are low, this alters the chemical balance of your body, especially the function of your thyroid, which determines your metabolism. When your thyroid is not working properly, your adrenal gland takes over to release powerful chemicals such as cortisone that can destroy vital organs such as the heart and liver.

Having no expectations of your life fosters boredom, despair and hopelessness. All of these attitudes are life-threatening. Low expectations deaden hope and the possibility of miracles. To heal many illnesses, it is necessary to work with raising expectations rather than, as many doctors do, to lower expectations to defend themselves legally in the name of statistics. Each cancer patient is unique. Hopelessness and a lack of expectancy is not something that overcomes you; it is the result of your choice to not see the possibilities for healing in even the gravest illness.

With some illnesses such as terminal cancer, chronic heart disease and arthritis, families often accept the medical opinion that the situation is hopeless and that the patient will not survive or will not return to health. Remissions from any and all illnesses do occur when the patient is sufficiently motivated. Miracles are more frequent than we realize, if the patient and those around him or her continue to hope.

Many illnesses for which traditional medicine has offered no hope can be healed if work is done to encourage expectation, emotion and imagination. When a terminally ill patient chooses to die, however, this death is not a failure. Death is no competition in which we win or lose; it is a natural process which can be the ultimate healing if we choose it and prepare for it. Hope is the willingness to look at a situation, to see the real possibilities that are there, and then to allow these possibilities to come alive for you in the present.

Healing can occur at any time. Even the gravely ill person can accomplish the inner process of forgiveness and release that brings inner peace. When family members assume the patient will die and there is no hope, it is harder for the patient to hope and to fight for life.

In their research with cancer patients, the Simontons discovered that a hopeful outlook that expected recovery from cancer was an even better predictor of the outcome of an illness than was the severity of it. Each of the patients who recovered from cancer had used various types of treatment. What they had in common was a high level of expectancy. The cancer patients who recovered decided for whatever reason that they would live. These patients had high expectations for their recovery. They were troublemakers who rebelled against any consensus of beliefs that said they would not live. Expectancy apparently triggered a chemical process within the bodies of these cancer patients that helped mobilize their immune systems to heal them.

One helpful way of raising expectancy is to stimulate the imagination by imaging those things you expect to accomplish and to have happen in your future. This can be done with the help of a meditation tape or as part of a daily imaging healing meditation. Another helpful technique is to observe the natural expectancy of the elements–fire, water, air and earth–and use this to heal you. Use a little magic to imagine what color, texture and taste the expectancy of these elements have, and then bottle and use it as another healing medicine.

Many people hold the belief that "cancer means death." Then the news that they have cancer can be like a death sentence, and researchers have found that the progress of cancer in the body is often accelerated when the patient is given the diagnosis of cancer. This acceleration could be prevented by a healthier, more realistic attitude toward the disease. Believing that the cancer is not necessarily fatal allows the patient to choose whether to make the life changes necessary to become well again.

The hopelessness of family or friends can have a depressing impact upon a patient. Those who love an ill person do him or her a service by maintaining a hopeful attitude. The tendency to condescend and to rob the ill of their power should be definitely avoided. Instead of being pampered and catered to, it is often more hopeful and encouraging to a patient if he or she is expected to be active and to exercise his or her own powers of self-discipline and decision making. Cancer, heart and arthritis patients do not need inactivity. Through activity, these patients can find and express their own uniqueness more freely.

If you have no expectations from life, you risk becoming ill. We are often encouraged to lower our expectations by others who are well meaning and afraid that we will get hurt if we expect too much. These people do not realize that expectancy is essential to our health and our chances of healing. Expectation is the result of imagination, which is a feminine energy. One of the things which block expectations is a rejection of yin or feminine energy because of cultural values that deny or devalue the feminine in us all. To allow expectation, you may have to face your refusal to be fully and wholly human by reclaiming your ability to imagine and to expect healing, magic and miracles to transform your life.

Gratitude

Gratitude is not something we usually associate with illness; it is assumed that no one should feel grateful during an illness. However, the person who rejoices in self-healing and growth is far ahead of the one who refuses to acknowledge the help and healing that is available from other people, modern medicine and creative healing forces.

Gratitude should not be thought of as a penance to God but rather an opportunity to see things in a higher, more evolved way. It is more than thankfulness, it is an opportunity to express an appreciation of oneself and for the powerful forces of healing within and around us. Gratitude is a secret healer of great power; it helps to lift and lighten us. Gratitude heals because it blocks the feelings of self-pity and self-importance in victims and martyrs. You cannot continue to be a victim or a martyr if you are grateful; the feelings of gratitude and self-pity are mutually exclusive.

Chapter Five

Stress and Illness

A disease or symptom represents your body's way of symbolizing your reaction and specific attitude to something you consider stressful. Contrary to popular opinion, stress is not something that is unavoidable or that just happens to you over which you have no control; to be stressed is a choice. The choice to live a stressed life is often also a choice for illness. Choosing stress or peace is important, because it not only influences our physical health, but also the course of our human and spiritual development. The more fully realized we are, the more we come to a position of detached inner peacefulness and freedom from stress.

Whether you are stressed by any particular circumstance depends upon how you choose to focus upon each of the three factors that determine a stressful situation; the stressful event itself, your interpretation of it, and your reaction to it. You can, for instance, choose not to participate in what you know will be a stressful event, such as a mountain climb. You can interpret a life event such as a divorce as a challenge or as the end of your life. You can choose to react to some usually stressful event in a new way, for instance by using some form of relaxation such as meditation that is incompatible with stress.

Stress is a prison of your own making that can ruin your health when and if you choose to feel oppressed and victimized by events.

You can choose to feel hopeless or helpless about the death a spouse , or you can see it as a challenge to build a new life. Rush hour traffic can be seen as time to enjoy some classical music, or as a battle. A job transfer can mean you see yourself as a pawn in the chess board of life, or as having been given an opportunity to make a new start in your own way.

Research shows that illness and even death can follow in the wake of grief, unrequited love, financial losses, humiliation and other emotionally painful events. There is a relationship between stress and illness; approximately 70% of physical illness develops at periods of time when individuals feel helpless or hopeless under what they interpret as stressful circumstances. The incidence of illness in the year following the stress of a divorce is twelve times higher than the norm and even the death rate of widowers is ten times higher than average in the first year of bereavement. (Seligman, 1975)

Research shows that although there is a great relationship between stress and illness in many peoples' lives, the correlation between stressful life events and illness is not statistically significant (about .30 at best). Thus, the stress of life increases rates of illness only in some people. Researchers such as Kobasa (1979) have demonstrated that many people do not become ill despite stressful circumstances in their lives. The emphasis in "stress and illness" research has shifted toward studying those factors that make some individuals resistant to illness.

Researchers have in vain tried to make a direct connection between stress and illness, because they could not determine why the same stress triggers different disorders in various individuals, and why others remain totally unaffected and healthy under stress. The stress experiments upon rats in laboratories do not apply directly to human beings, because humans have greater abilities to cope than do rats. Rats lack the human ability to reflect upon and choose their interpretation of events.

What is Stress?

Stress has been defined as the specific response of a body to any demand. (Selye, 1977) Stress is a stimulus or force that produces a reaction. Stress is any life experience that causes physical, mental, and emotional change in the individual that results in a state of internal imbalance. It can be physical, such as an injury or exposure to temperature extremes or toxic materials; or psychological, such as the emotional response of anxiety, depression, anger, guilt, or hurt engendered by a potential threat; it can even be pleasure derived from an exciting experience. The stress experienced depends not upon the agent that produces it, but upon the person involved and the way he or she reacts.

In many cases, when our feelings, such as anxiety, run strong and are prolonged, our bodies undergo specific alterations. When we experience powerful feelings of grief, hate, anger, fear or depression, either consciously or suppressed, actual physical changes occur; sometimes such that our bodies express these emotions as illness.

Some of the common ways people react to stress are by an increase in pulse rate and an increased tendency to perspire. People also become more irritable, less able to concentrate, and sometimes suffer from insomnia when under stress. They also have an increased desire to move about. Distress is present when the adaptive mechanisms of an individual are taxed or strained.

Stress is not something from which one might anticipate a specific bodily response. On the contrary, a specific stressor may yield almost any kind of response, from invention or creativity to surrender or death. The bodily responses of any group of people to a stressful event such as loud noise would differ widely; for some people there may be changes in heart beat and blood pressure and adrenaline release, for others only a restlessness and slight irritability, while still others may react with no physical changes.

Many important discoveries and works of art have been made under circumstances of stress. Reaction to stress may be measured in terms of success or the maintenance of equilibrium, as well as in terms of failure of adaption and disease. There is great variety in the ways people adapt to stress, and therefore the mechanisms that serve stress must be similarly numerous. The human species' special ability to react to symbols as though to significant events enriches our existence, but at the same time increases our ability to perceive threats. Some of the situations that can be perceived as threatening are repetitious, nonchallenging job situations, or changes in environment or relationships.

Selye, whose pioneer work brought into focus the concept of stress, emphasized the need to honor individual differences in response to stress. This he said was really a matter of deciding what style of life was right for you. He compared people to other species, saying you "can't make a racehorse out of a turtle." When a "turtle-type" human tried to live a "racehorse-type" life, it could kill him or her. The reverse was also true; a "racehorse-type" person should not try to live a "turtle-type" life, for that too would place a person under terrible distress. Selye emphasized the need for an individual to overcome stress through honoring his or her uniqueness. (Selye, 1977)

Stress and Immune Deficiency Diseases

Selye emphasized the need to address the underlying stress rather than merely to treat an illness with medications. Our health is our aliveness and therefore real healing is inside of us and has to deal with anything that interferes with our growth and aliveness. Healing in the future will be more involved with the use of the mind, because the mind is the common factor in the defense system of the body. It is the mind through its brain chemistry that controls the release of peptides and neuro-peptides that govern the endocrine, immune and lymphatic systems. All these systems affect immune deficiency diseases. In symbolic terms, the immune system symbolizes our defense against the world around us in times of stress.

The breakdown of this defense leaves you powerless. This powerlessness starts with spiritual powerlessness which leads to emotional powerlessness, hopelessness and self-pity. The lymphatic system moves garbage out of your body. When you harbor emotions and do not think and feel, this system becomes stressed because it is clogged with toxins.

The endocrine system governs growth especially during childhood and adolescence. When you refuse to grow up and stay a child or adolescent emotionally, mentally and spiritually, you leave yourself open to anxiety. Anxiety is denied or unrecognized anger, fear, hurt or self-pity. The anxiety of this stagnation, when chronic, is closely related to a broad spectrum of autoimmune diseases which includes arthritis, diabetes, chronic fatigue syndrome, multiple sclerosis, lupus, candidiasis and cancer.

This chronic state is related to the martyr's game of silent suffering whose most dominant feelings are self-pity, self-importance and righteous anger. The anxiety of martyrdom causes the endocrine system to release lactic acid which the immune and lymphatic system have to handle and move. In response to anxiety, the brain releases tryptophan, a growth hormone which in adults can trigger growths like tumors, diabetes, or cancer. Anxiety also triggers serotonin which in excess can have harmful effects upon muscles and tissues.

Serotonin is stimulated to produce a calm clarity when you are anxious, but if your anxiety is prolonged, serotonin can begin to attack and debilitate the immune system. Then the body appears to be attacking itself, to reflect the state of attack you perceive from the outer environment while in a state of anxiety. It is reacting to an imaginary enemy–God, life, the spouse or boss you really feel should be punished or blamed. To break such a cycle requires replacing the source of the anxiety–the feelings of self-pity, powerlessness, refusal to release emotions, refusal to grow up and accept responsibility–with beliefs and attitudes that support you. (Lazaris, *Escaping the Suffocating Web of Anxiety* (tape))

Stress and Illness

What seems to produce illness is a prolonged or extreme emotional response to any stress. Death of a loved one or divorce requires undergoing an emotional stress of grieving and readjusting to a new life without that person, but this becomes disease-producing only when it is prolonged or extreme.

Hans Selye cited three stages of stress. The first is the alarm stage where your body releases chemicals into the blood stream to prepare you to act. Stage two is that of apparent adaption to an ongoing stress such as a loud noise, although the body continues to pump chemicals into the blood, and maintain high blood pressure and muscle tension. It is in the stage of adaption that the response of the body becomes specific. The particular conflict goes to that organ, system or physiological process that is best designed to take care of that kind of threat. The third stage is exhaustion, if the threat or inner symbolic conflict continues. Unless there is resolution, your body will get ill or die. You can only endure pumping these powerful chemicals and maintaining that state of readiness for so long. The endorphins that are present to help you cope with, say, shame can be destructive if that shame is not healed and released. If you live as though you had your foot on the emergency brake, it should not be surprising when your vehicle wears out sooner.

Stress can be seen as your body's response to symbolic experiences that are the result of mental interpretations. Mind and body are one. When an internal conflict is not resolved within your mind and emotions, it is projected out upon your body where it is then represented back to you in a symbolic way.

Healthy Ways of Dealing with Stress

The modern world encourages people to stop feeling, thinking and being aware of their stress. Doing is emphasized rather than feeling, thinking and being, and enjoying life. Struggling is valued over solving problems with elegance. Since stress begins within, there are some important steps you can take to avoid the inner conflict that produces it. These steps are:

(1) End self-pity and the powerlessness, defenselessness and anger that goes with it.

(2) Start feeling and thinking, and get rid of any harbored emotions that poison your body. Feel your connection to others and your divinity.

(3) Grow up spiritually by not martyring yourself to a patriarchal system. Develop a living, breathing, personal relationship to God/Goddess/All There Is.

(4) Be alive by trusting those who are trustworthy and being loving, showing enthusiasm and expectation.

(5) Accept all parts of yourself, your child or adolescent with love, forgiveness and understanding.

(6) Don't expect yourself to be perfect. You are human and perfectionism leads to failure and a static life.

(7) Escape anxiety by facing and releasing the feelings beneath it; fear, anger, shame, hurt and self-pity.

(8) Value yourself and commit yourself to expressing your uniqueness through taking responsibility for your choices, beliefs and attitudes.

Those people who remain healthy while living successful lives can teach us much. Integrating various theoretical and practical ideas, Kobasa proposed that hardiness in the face of stress is a constellation of three personality characteristics–commitment, control and challenge–that function as a resistance in the face of stressful life events. Persons high in hardiness easily commit themselves to what they are doing (rather than feeling alienated), generally believe that they can at least partially control events (rather than feeling powerless), and regard change to be a normal challenge or impetus to development (rather than a threat). (Kobasa and Pucetti, 1983, p. 840.) It is important to make a distinction between exerting appropriate control in a situation, *dominion*, and trying to forcefully take control over a situation, *domination*.

Dominion over one's body and health is healthy, while domination is not.

In her first study of hardiness, Kobasa (1979) examined executives under high levels of stress and divided them into groups with either high or low rates of illness. Hardiness scores, derived from scores on several personality questionnaires, differentiated between the groups in the expected manner. The executives with low rates of illness had higher hardiness scores than those with high rates of illness. In a subsequent study using a more powerful prospective method, executives' hardiness scores predicted whether they would later contract fewer or more illnesses. (Kobasa, Maddi and Kahn, 1982)

The stress reaction during a passing challenge or crisis is not the same as chronic or acute stress in which there is an extreme or prolonged emotional response that could cause illness. Periods of stimulation or crisis in your life and even periods of illness can be a time of profound personal transformation. Such times of crisis or illness can offer you and those about you the opportunity to make major life changes that are breakthroughs to richer, fuller lives.

Hardy people are those who are able to evaluate what others see as stressful events, such as death, divorce or unemployment, as not so meaningless, overwhelming and undesirable as they might appear to be. In reaction to this evaluation, hardy people are able to interact with and transform the events of their lives into less stressful forms. People with hardy personality dispositions therefore avoid those illness-provoking biological states that Selye called adaptation exhaustion (Selye, 1956) or depressed immunological surveillance. They are able to remain healthy while experiencing events that would be debilitating for others. The key to a healthy adaption to stress seems to lie in evaluating events with a healthy detachment that allows for creative power, challenge and commitment.

This study of persons who do not fall ill despite considerable stress suggests that some personality factors may have much to do with staying healthy. Those people who encountered stress rather than avoiding or resisting it were committed to their lives and had a generalized *sense of purpose* that allowed them to identify with and find meaningful the events, things, and persons of their environment. These committed individuals have invested enough in themselves, their relationships and their social or work life that they cannot easily give up under pressure. These people have a relationship with themselves and their environment that includes active involvement rather than passivity and avoidance.

When a hardy person meets a stressful life event, he or she evaluates this event and copes with it in different ways than a person who has no such hardiness. For example, a hardy male executive having to deal with a job transfer will approach the necessary readjustment is his life with:

(a) a clear sense of his values, goals and capabilities and a belief in their importance (commitment to rather than alienation from self)

(b) a strong tendency toward active involvement with his environment (vigorousness rather than passivity).

Hence the hardy executive does more than passively acquiesce to the job transfer. He throws himself actively into the new situation, utilizing his inner resource to make it his own.

Another important characteristic of this hardy executive is an unshakable sense of meaningfulness and ability to evaluate the impact of the transfer in terms of a general life plan with its established priorities. The healthy executive chooses to see life as meaningful, rather than meaningless. For him the job transfer means a change that can be transformed into a potential step in the right direction in his overall career plan and also provide his family with a stimulating change.

Committed people have a belief system that minimizes the perceived threat of any given stressful life event. They encounter their stressful environment rather than do battle with it; they are adventurers rather than strugglers or warriors. Any stressful situation is lessened by a sense of purpose that prevents them from giving up on their social involvements and integrity under pressure. Committed persons feel an involvement with others that serves as a generalized buffer against the impact of stress. (Antonovsky, 1974) They have an ability to turn to others for assistance in times of stress. If they are involved in a divorce or death of a spouse, they turn to friends, social institutions and the family for the comfort and support they need.

Staying healthy under stress is critically dependent on a strong sense of commitment to yourself and your growth. This commitment recognizes you have unique goals, talents and priorities that are important in dealing with stress. This kind of commitment is what Hans Selye calls "altruistic egoism." What he meant by this term was a healthy self-love that ultimately leads to a love for others. In doing your own thing and seeking your own purpose, you remain healthy and ultimately you are most helpful to others as well.

Committed people know and continue to seek their own life purposes. They make wise decisions in stressful situations based upon their own personal values and goals. (Kobasa, 1979) An internal rather than external source (locus) of control allows the hardy executive to greet the job transfer with integrity. Although the transfer may have been initiated in an office above him, the actual course it takes depends on how he handles it. The hardy executive is not threatened by change because he actively determines the consequences it brings about.

In contrast, the executive low in hardiness will react to a job transfer with less sense of personal resource, more acquiescence, more encroachment of meaninglessness, and a conviction that the change has been externally determined with no possibility of control on his part. Thus, the less hardy executive perceives a transfer as more stressful than his hardy counterpart who is more in control of the process.

The control component of hardiness is a tendency to feel and act as if you are powerful in the face of any or all life events, even in the most threatening of circumstances. The assurance that you are powerful implies the perception of yourself as consciously creating the events of your life through the exercise of your imagination, knowledge, beliefs and choice. Conscious creativity enhances stress resistance by increasing the likelihood that events will be experienced as a natural outgrowth of your actions and therefore, not foreign, unexpected and overwhelming experiences. In terms of coping, a sense of power leads to actions that can transform events into something consistent with your life plan and goals and therefore less jarring and stressful.

Additional support for the conscious power aspect of the hardiness theory comes from studies of college students, paralyzed accident patients, and women who were suspected to have cervical cancer. Those students who believed in an internal locus of power had a significantly lower correlation between stressful life events and illness than did subjects who believed they were externally controlled. (Johnson and Sarason, 1978) Among patients who were paralyzed as a result of an accident, those who did best in rehabilitation were those who took responsibility for their part in causing the accident that resulted in their paralysis, and therefore they took more responsibility for their rehabilitation. (Bulman and Wortman, 1977)

Finally, a series of clinical studies also demonstrates the importance of a sense of power, rather than a sense of hopelessness or despair in the face of life events. In the work of Schmale and Iker (1966), a study was done of women with a history of abnormal cervical pap smears who were hospitalized for an extensive diagnostic procedure designed to establish the presence or absence of malignancy. Before the results of the procedure were available, the investigators interviewed and evaluated each woman for "hopelessness potential" and recent actual reactions of hopelessness in the face of stress events, and made a prognosis on the basis of this factor. Their predictions of cervical cancer on the basis of two characteristics of hopeless potential were confirmed as correct by pathological diagnosis in 74% of all the women studied. (Kobasa, 1982)

The third component of hardiness is that of challenge, which expresses itself as the belief that change rather than stability is normal in life and that anticipated changes are interesting incentives to growth rather than threats to security. If you view changes as stimulating, colorful events rather than as threatening, then your open, flexible attitude toward those changes makes them much easier.

Studies upon students showed that those who saw life as a stimulating adventure were less likely to experience it as stressful than those who viewed life as a battle or a struggle. (Kobasa, Maddi, and Kahn, 1982) This research supports the theory that there is no direct correspondence between stressful events and illness. Human beings are not passive victims of illness. Their choices and beliefs have much to do with their health or illness.

Correspondence between Illness and Specific Attitude to Stress

Several scientific studies have proven that specific attitudes and feelings toward stressful events are associated with eighteen illnesses frequently considered psychosomatic, including asthma and duodenal ulcers.

In 1952, a study was done at the New York Hospital with Cornell University on 128 patients with one of twelve symptoms or diseases to study how specific attitudes were related to each symptom or psychosomatic disease. In this study, a correlation was found between the attitudes of sick people who represented twelve different illnesses and their actual bodily symptoms of illness. This study was based entirely on the patients' statements about their feelings concerning stressful life circumstances that precipitated their illnesses; no subconscious materials from dreams or imagery work were elicited. (Grace and Graham, 1952)

In this initial study, the following symptoms or diseases as related to stressful life situations were studied: urticaria, eczema, cold hands, vasomotor rhinitis and asthma, diarrhea, constipation, nausea and vomiting, duodenal ulcer, migraine, arterial hypertension, and low back pain. It was found that each of these conditions was associated with a particular completely conscious attitude toward the precipitating situation. There were, in other words, physiological changes specific to each attitude. These changes are biologically appropriate to the attitude they accompany.

It was proposed by the researchers that we need to refine our definitions of "emotion" to mean "an attitude with its associated physiological changes." It appeared that in most cases the attitude which a sick person held such as resentment, hostility or revenge is accompanied by the function of the physiological processes with which it is associated. Resentment, defined as a feeling of indignant displeasure because of something regarded as an insult, often was accompanied with urticaria, a disease of the skin characterized by transient eruptions resembling wheals. Regret, the wish something had not happened, is often associated with vomiting where the individual tries to free him- or herself of something for which he or she feels entirely responsible. Revenge, to inflect punishment, injury or loss in return for or in retaliation, is often associated with ulcers in which something is "eating away upon oneself" that one feels unable to control.

A more extensive study was done in 1963 as a follow-up to this initial study. It used various methods to control for bias-blind interviewers and impartial, nonmedical judges . This follow-up study, done at the University of Wisconsin by Graham, found there was significant evidence that 18 psychosomatic diseases could be differentiated by what a patient said concerning their emotional reactions to precipitating events. (Graham, Lundy, Benjamin, Kabler, Lewis, Kunish and Graham, 1962)

The results of both of these studies are exciting because they suggest that in a wide number of "psychosomatic" illnesses the symptoms involved are symbolic of the attitudes and beliefs that the sick person has at the time the illness occurs. Both studies limited their research to the conscious attitudes of subjects who were ill. These attitudes were defined as the patient's interpretation of precipitating situations, and their response to them–in other words, to the individuals' feelings about what was happening to them and what they wished to do about it. The second study also included hypertension, multiple sclerosis, migraine, ulcerative colitis, hyperthyroidism and metabolic edema.

Grace and Graham (Grace and Graham, 1952, 1962) found that in most cases there was a relationship between the illness process and the patient's reaction to stress. An individual developed one specific illness because it symbolized or was appropriate to his or her specific emotional and mental attitude to stress. The person with lower back pain had pain in the lower back not because he strained his back, but because he considered his "load too heavy" or that people expected too much of him.

The hypothesis that particular attitudes are associated with particular diseases was tested by determining whether the attitude which judges selected as characteristic of patients were, in fact, the attitudes predicted by the hypothesis. Judges selected the attitude predicted to be associated with a patient's disease proportionally more often than not. The judges concluded that their findings were evidence that psychosomatic diseases could be differentiated by patient-stated reactions to stressful life situations.

The eighteen predicted attitudes for certain illnesses were these (Graham, Lundy, Benjamin, Kabler, Wesis, Kunish and Graham, 1962):

1. Urticaria. Felt he was taking a beating and was helpless to do anything about it.

2. Ulcerative colitis. Felt he was being injured and degraded and wished he could get rid of the responsible agent.

3. Eczema. Felt he was being frustrated and could do nothing about it except take it out on himself.

4. Acne. Felt he was being picked on or at and wanted to be let alone.

5. Psoriasis. Felt there was a constant gnawing at him and that he had to put up with it.

6. Bronchial asthma. Felt left out in the cold and wanted to shut the person or situation out.

7. Hyperthyroidism. Felt he might lose somebody or something he loved and took care of, and tried to prevent the loss.

8. Vomiting. Felt something wrong had happened, usually something for which he felt responsible, and wished it hadn't happened.

9. Duodenal Ulcer. Felt deprived of what was due him and wanted to get even.

10. Constipation. Felt in a situation from which nothing good could come but kept on with it grimly.

11. Hypertension. Felt threatened with harm and had to be ready for anything.

12. Migraine. Felt something had to be achieved and then relaxed after the effort.

13. Multiple Sclerosis. Felt he was forced to undertake some kind of physical activity, especially hard work, and wanted not to.

14. Metabolic Edema. Felt he was carrying a heavy load and wanted somebody else to carry all or part of it.

15. Rheumatoid Arthritis. Felt tied down and wanted to get free.

16. Raynaud's Disease. Wanted to take hostile physical action.

17. Regional Enteritis. Felt he had received something harmful and wanted to get rid of it.

18. Low Backache. Wanted to run away.

Wolf and Goodell had previously identified many reactions in the body that mirrored an individual's mental-emotional response to an imagined or subconscious stress. These scientists perceived that disease symptoms may be ways that the body adapts to a perceived threat, as if the regulating mechanism in the individual had responded to an actual physical threat. They attributed this "as if" response to an earlier period of evolutionary development that is inappropriate in the present environment. Although these responses are inappropriate and disease-producing physically, they accurately describe symbolically the underlying mental and emotional conflict. (Wolf and Goodell, 1968)

Many illnesses such as coronary artery and heart disease, cancer and diabetes are not usually considered "psychosomatic" diseases. This discovery suggests that not only psychosomatic illnesses but many others have a psychological correspondence to the physiological disease process. It is likely that the characteristic attitudes which accompany any particular disease process will be more accurately and precisely defined through further research, and this will make predictions of diagnosis based on beliefs and attitudes more reliable.

More study, however, should be done on extreme and pro-longed emotional-mental states. For instance, the attitude of those who develop ulcers may have more to do with a constant state of fear because of a need to control to be safe, and this may involve an overly vigilant attitude that may be related to feeling overburdened or vengeful.

Cobb and Rose (1973), for example, found that ulcers were twice as frequent among air traffic controllers as among pilots. The pilots may experience less stress because they have more control over their planes than do the air traffic controllers. More young men than women acquire ulcers and this may be related to cultural pressures on young men to control their feelings and to live up to a cultural image of what a man should be.

Wolf and Goodell described the following correspondences between the attitudes of individuals in stressful situations and the physical illnesses that resulted:

In duodenal ulcer the physical process symbolizes a readiness to devour. The gastric behavior of a peptic ulcer patient is as if he or she were always devouring or receiving nourishment. Stressful circumstances in the lives of patients with peptic ulcers, especially those which arouse hostile feelings, may be associated with an increase in the secretion of gastric acid and pepsin. Those who have studied patients with peptic ulcers find them often to be competitive and resentful. These people may also have a great fear that they will not get enough nurturing, food being symbolic of a need for love, acceptance, etc. Typical comments from those who suffer from peptic ulcer are: "I wanted to get even." "I wanted to get back at him." "I wanted revenge." "I did it for spite."

In diabetes mellitus the physical process is symbolic of starvation. A metabolic change occurs in which there is a tendency to substitute fat for glucose as fuel for body. The circumstance which would be most appropriate under such a response is starvation. For years psychiatrists have pointed out the frequent association of obesity to diabetes and the psychological identification in the minds of diabetic patients of food with love. Juvenile diabetes is often preceded by a period of obesity, and there is often evidence of love deprivation during the infantile period. Hinkel and his associates found that a prominent though often suppressed or repressed conviction of diabetic patients, especially juveniles, was that of having been starved of maternal love. "I never got the love I needed when I was a child." "All of the sweetness and joy has gone out of my life."

In asthma an attack symbolizes or is as if one were suffocating or going inward to a safe place where you would not have to face some situation. The hidden wish is that of an intense feeling that some situation would go away or that somebody else would take over the responsibility for it. The intense feeling here is one of being smothered or stifled by a dominating person or situation. Typical statements made by asthma patients interviewed are these: "I wanted them to go away." "I didn't want to have anything to do with it." "I just couldn't face it."

Low back pain is related to a desire to carry out some action involving movement of the entire body, but without the actual carrying out of this action. This activity usually is walking or running away. A typical statement made by those with lower back pain is: "I wanted to run away, or just get out of there." The sufferer of back pain may consider his or her "load too heavy" or that "they are expecting too much of me" or "they have given me too much to do."

Eczema occurred when people felt that they were being interfered with or prevented from doing something and could think of no way to deal with the frustration. There was a preoccupation in the patients with the interference of those whom they felt were thwarting them, rather than with a way of dealing with the problem. Typical statements were: "I wanted to make my mother understand, but I can't" or "I couldn't do what I wanted to but there wasn't anything I could do about it."

Diarrhea expresses an impatience, a wish to get on with it or be done with it or to get rid of something connected with one's life. Typical statements include: "I wanted to get finished with it, or be done with it."

Constipation is accompanied an attitude of grim determination to hold on or to carry on, even though faced with an unsolvable problem. Typical statements were these: "I have to keep with this, but I know I'm not going to like it," or "This is never going to get better but I won't quit," or "I have to hold on to what I have."

Nausea and vomiting correspond to an individual's effort to restore things to their original situation as if nothing had ever happened. Usually the individual felt responsible for what had happened. Typical statements were : "I wish it hadn't happened." "I made a mistake." "I wish things were the way they were before." "I am sorry I did it."

With migraine there is a constriction of the blood vessels and nerves of the head. The attitude that corresponds to this constriction is one of dread of being found wrong, associated with striving to gain approval by working longer and harder than others. Typical statements were: "I had to get it done." "I had to meet a deadline." "I had a million things to do before lunch." "I was trying to get all these things accomplished." (Wolf and Goodell, 1968)

Identifying and Taking Control of Stressful Situations

Stress is avoidable if you remember there is always a positive reaction that can be chosen for every situation you can find yourself in, even the most dire such as imprisonment. The most dramatic example of this was Viktor Frankl's choice to forgive his oppressors and to use his concentration camp experience to inspire himself and others. Events do not cause stress, interpretations of events do. By reinterpreting the events of your life in more peaceful ways, you can avoid unnecessary stress. Suppose your car breaks down and you need to get to work; you have a choice of how to interpret this event. You can see yourself as a victim. You can get angry and start pounding on the car and feel hopeless, helpless or victimized. Or, you can call the neighbor and get a ride, choosing to see this as an opportunity to car pool, or take a bus and relax instead.

The decision to feel threatened can create a threat. When you interpret situations as threatening to your safety and well being, your body will experience stress. Stressed people are less creative or intuitive, so they are less productive, because solutions to problems that could be understood intuitively and creatively are unavailable. Being stressed can ultimately lead to illness, because the immune system is compromised and weakened in states of exhaustion. If you choose to interpret situations as threatening, you will actually create real threats to your job security and health.

The death of a spouse, for instance, may be interpreted by some individuals as leaving them nothing to live for. Grieving is necessary and healthy, but an extreme and prolonged hopeless attitude can severely compromise the immune system and contribute to illness and death. Another interpretation to a spouse's death could be, "This is a chance to explore new relationships and do things I felt I could not do before."

Stress and Needs

When your needs are not met, your body is stressed. Maslow was the first psychologist to speak of a spectrum of needs. In Maslow's needs theory, the need of survival/security is the basis for the fulfillment of the other needs of belonging, self-esteem, creativity/productivity, socialness, knowing and spirituality. His system was a lateral one, in which one need built upon another.

The body can be seen as a symbolic spectrum of needs that when stressed or conflicted is reflected as illness in the chakra areas of the body that symbolize that need. For instance, if you have unmet security needs, you are likely to have problems with your feet, hands, lower back or tail bone, the areas that symbolize security issues. When these needs are not met genuinely, they are often met by the false substitute of control over or domination of the area that symbolizes that need, and you are then more likely to develop health problems in that area.

Your body symbolically represents the fulfillment or frustration of your needs. This symbolic system is not just a lateral system where one need builds and depends upon the lower one (as Maslow thought), but a vertical, spiral one in which the fulfillment of any need affects all the others. Higher needs such as spirituality and knowing affect but do not depend upon lower ones such as security or self-esteem. Your needs interact to help fulfill each other better. When one need is satisfied to an increased degree, such as knowing or intuition, this affects your creativity/productivity need, which in turn affects your spirituality.

The state of your health symbolizes the way your needs are being satisfied or frustrated. Illness occurs when needs are frustrated or blocked. It is important to recognize your needs and give yourself permission to realize and express them.

Left/Right-Sided Symptoms and Stress

An illness tells you that you are imbalanced, off center or out of harmony in some important area of your life. Where a bodily symptom is located, on the right or left side, often tells you whether you are imbalanced in your yin (feminine) or yang (masculine) energies. The wisdom of centuries of Eastern Medicine is based on the concept that all illnesses are a reflection of an imbalance of yin and yang energies in the body. While Chinese medicine stops short of indicating the mental, emotional and spiritual qualities of yin and yang which these symptoms symbolize, Taoist medicine relates problems with certain organs to certain negative emotions, and their healing to their positive opposite:

lungs	sadness, grief or sorrow / courage, letting go
kidneys	fear / gentleness
liver	anger, aggression / kindness
heart	impatience, arrogance, hastiness, violence or cruelty / joy, honor, sincerity
spleen	worry, sympathy or pity / fairness, compassion and centering.

While this correspondence may differ for left-handed people, generally the right side of the body and the left side of the forehead reflect the analytic, active and verbal left hemisphere of the brain. When symptoms occur in these areas, they often have to do with imbalanced masculine yang energy. Problems in these areas also often involve conflicts with a father or other male figure.

Generally the left side of the body and the right side of the forehead reflect the right side of the brain, the intuitive, imaginative and creative side. Symptoms in these areas often have to do with an imbalance of the yin or feminine energy. Problems with the left side of the body and the right side of the forehead are often related to a conflict with your mother or another woman, indicating too much negative or too little positive feminine energy.

Symptoms of illness are sometimes stimulated by the stress of a relationship. The specific attitude that has been identified with Raynard's disease is the desire to, and the suppression of the impulse to, hit someone. Sonia, who had Raynard's disease and scleroderma, said that she often felt an impulse to hit her husband but always suppressed it because she felt this was inconsistent with being a loving, Christian wife. Sonia suffered from pain on the left side of her face and neck, and in her right arm and leg, which almost totally immobilized her. Sonia is a right-handed 57-year-old woman who looks frail and older than her years.

Raynard's disease is an illness in which a person's hands and feet become blue and cold. In a defensive reaction to a perceived threat from the outside, the blood vessels constrict in the extremities to protect the body against blood loss from an attack by an enemy. Her fingers and feet were blue, hard and crusty. Sonia had lost the ends of two of her fingers and looked as though she were being gradually shrunk. She also suffered from candidiasis. Scleroderma is an autoimmune disease which causes the immune system to attack the connective tissues, organs and blood vessels.

The origin of Sonia's illness appeared to be her inner conflict over asserting herself against an oppressive husband. This conflict found its expression in pain on the left side of her head and the right side of her body, symbolizing a suppression or conflict with her assertive, out-going masculine energies. Sonia's husband John was a large man who often put her down by ignoring or embarrassing her, or treating her chauvinistically. Instead of defending herself and speaking up to him, Sonia shrunk back internally from him. Her body prepared to defend itself and contracted in preparation for a threatened attack. Since Sonia would not defend herself through self-assertion, her body continued to shrink and defend her symbolically through defensiveness.

Sonia's feelings toward her husband were projections of those she felt for her father. Sonia said her father had been an "ogre," who thought his children should be seen but not heard. Sonia did not wish to be like her mother who was quietly resentful, but by denying her anger projected it upon her body. Sonia was a fraternal twin who had trouble setting boundaries. She had allowed her twin sister to take the initiative in activities throughout their life.

Through imagery, relaxation, and rehearsals with music, Sonia began to express her anger at her husband more honestly and freely. Sonia felt she could not defend herself because she was less important than her husband. I urged her to change her belief system and to value herself more. When Sonia began to see herself as having the ability and esteem to defend herself against emotional abuse, she no longer was immobilized by fear and her symptoms began to disappear. Her hands turned from blue to pink within a short time.

A balanced life can be seen as one in which you give yourself permission to express both sides of yourself, the emotional-imaginative-yin side, and the understanding-assertive-yang side.

Repressed or supressed anger is behind almost every illness, and can be avoided if you express this anger cleanly. To release righteous anger, you have to first give up the payoff of feeling righteous before you can then process the underlying anger. To process guilt you have to give yourself permission to feel and release the anger hidden within it.

Overcoming Stress Through Relaxation and Meditation

One of the most effective ways to overcome stress is to practice some form of relaxation, and meditation is one of the most effective methods. Dr. Herbert Benson, studying the physical benefits of meditation, found that it tends to lower or normalize the blood pressure and pulse rate, and to decrease the level of stress hormones in the blood. Meditation also changes the brain wave patterns, showing a more relaxed, less excitable state of mind. These physical effects reflect changes in attitudes which can change the personality pattern of individuals from more stressful Type A modes of behavior to more relaxed, healthier personality behaviors. Anyone can practice some form of meditation that at least is simply a mental/physical relaxation technique, and for many can also be a form of spiritual focusing and centering.

The result, which Herbert Benson calls "the relaxation response," is a counterpart or opposite of the fight-or-flight stress response, so any method that elicits this response counteracts stress. The relaxation response is elicited through practices that have existed for centuries including Eastern meditative techniques and Western relaxation methods.

Eastern meditation practices contain four basic elements: a comfortable position; a quiet environment; repetition of a prayer, word, sound or phrase; and adoption of a receptive attitude when other thoughts come into the mind. Meditation becomes a spiritual practice when you focus your attention and mind upon a high spiritual ideal such as love or union, and listen or feel in communion with spiritual forces. (Benson, 1979) When you are consciously changing a specific and recurrent stress that you have identified, one of several relaxation exercises can be used. One effective relaxation technique is to talk to parts of your body from your feet on up, telling them to relax, or to visualize yourself being in a bubble of safety. Another technique is walking meditation, a Western form of focusing your mind while in action.

Relaxation is helpful, but even more effective over a long term is a regular period of meditation. Research on meditation has proven that certain kinds of meditation, particularly Transcendental Meditation (TM), reduce hypertension.

TM is the most widely practiced form of meditation in the Western world; it is effective to Westerners because it is a natural, gentle way to quiet the mind. Unlike other more rigid Eastern disciplines, it is a gentle receiving and letting go into peacefulness. The most common mantra, "Ohm mane padme Ohm," is used only as a vehicle, not a focus of attention. This mantra means the jewel in the heart of the lotus, or the spiritual self within the individual. When this vehicle gets you where you want to be, you leave it behind. TM has proven effective for people with hypertension, because the quietness of mind that results from it is maintained for extended periods of time, not just during meditation. Transcendental Meditation prevents and helps to transcend hypertension, but cannot replace the processing of the fearful conflicts necessary in that transcending.

How Society Affects Patterns of Illness

Individuals who identify with their society stay well as long as the values of their community are healthy. One such community is the Roseto community in Pennsylvania, studied in the 1960's by Stewart Wolf. Wolf found that the people in this community had an unusually low death rate from cardiovascular disease despite no significant differences from their neighbors in the risk factors related to heart disease, such as obesity, smoking, fat consumption, cholesterol level and lack of exercise. (Pellietier, 1979) From his findings, Wolf speculated that the difference in mortality rates had to be related to certain psychological factors. The most important, Wolf believed, was the active involvement, continual support and community participation of all its members. No one was ever abandoned in Roseto. During stressful times the community respected, cared for and included its elderly and sick. In this continuing study of Roseto, recent statistics show a marked increase in the death rate from heart disease as younger Rosetans married outside and the traditional community closeness declined. This study of Roseta supports the importance of being nurtured, needed, and productive in remaining healthy.

The sociologist Moss identified four different types of personality patterns that an individual can take in relationship to a group. These four patterns are the *identified*, the *alienated*, the *anomic* and the *autonomous* personalities. (Moss, 1973) Of these four types of people, those who are most alienated from others are most likely to become ill, and those who are most autonomous are most likely to stay well. Identified individuals stay well as long as the values and mores of the community in which they live are healthy ones. Hinkle found in studying the health of a group of office workers that, "Those who fit most comfortably in a given niche, who by background, temperament and physical characteristics seem best suited to the situation in life in which they find themselves, seem to do better in terms or overall health." (Moss, 1973)

On the other hand, identification with some groups in modern society may increase your susceptibility to disease. There are two main obstacles to eliminating Type A behavior in our society. The first obstacle is that people see Type A behavior as paying off in the short run, at least in increased productivity and achievement, if not in personal happiness. Secondly, being a Type A person in many ways is seen as desirable behavior in the United States and in many other industrialized countries as well. Often it is only after a person has a heart attack that he or she is forced to slow down and become less aggressive, hostile and competitive. (Price, 1982)

In modern industrial societies, the hardy, autonomous people are often the most healthy because they reject the norms of a society that may be unhealthy, such as excessive competitiveness. Hardy, autonomous people live by their own goals and inner principles. They have the integrity to overcome stress through a commitment to their uniqueness and a willingness to see stressful events as challenges to grow rather than as insurmountable obstacles.

Chapter Six

Befriending Your Subconscious Mind

The body and the subconscious both speak to us in symbols. The symbols of the body point out areas of conflict; every symptom of the body from a small cut on the finger to a cancerous tumor has a symbolic meaning. We can use the subconscious to heal and to give meaning to the symbolism of our bodies. If we listen to these messages, we can respond to them, preventing and healing illness. Many people fear even to consider the subconscious, and many deny that meaning exists there.

When people fear or deny themselves access to the understanding available in the subconscious, illness has only an evil meaning. In the language of the subconscious, illness is not just a dark, evil thing, it is an opportunity–a signal that an inner change is needed. The crippled or sick figure in mythology, in dreams and in waking life always indicates that something needs to be faced and released. The wheezing of asthma signals, for instance, that grief or fear exists and needs to be expressed and released. Our subconscious minds are the bridge between our bodies and our minds; they store and bring into physical reality our thoughts, feelings, motivations and self-image.

Your subconscious can be your best friend or your worst enemy, depending on what you store within it. If you store destructive emotions and thoughts there, it is your worst enemy.

Your subconscious mind creates your physical reality out of the belief systems that you place within it. You may or may not be consciously aware of these beliefs. Part of healing is a process of "raising your level of consciousness" by learning what is presently in the subconscious; what is stored within your subconscious mind is brought to the surface and recognized so it can be understood and released if appropriate.

The subconscious mind can be compared to creative soil that accepts all of your beliefs, no matter how crazy. What you believe to be true is stored in your subconscious, becoming true for you whether it is true or not. If your thoughts and feelings are negative such as "Don't love, you will only get hurt," or "Don't give, you will only be used," then the subconscious will honor them and serve the purpose expressed in those thoughts. It is not that one belief is wrong and another is right, but that one works and produces health while another does not. Criticism and judgement of yourself hurts you and others, while acceptance of yourself and others does not.

The subconscious mind is feared and demeaned by many. It is often seen as a throwback to our origins–something we have to lift ourselves out of. At best, the subconscious is seen as a servant, at worst a slave or enemy. Another perspective considers the subconscious as the access point to higher evolution and spiritual development. The subconscious can be considered a friend, a co-worker and co-creator in our journeys of spiritual and human development.

Retrieving Your Power of Choice
From the Subconscious

If you believe that you create your reality, including your health, then you also have to be responsible for what is stored in your subconscious, including your motives and self-image. Those who believe they are motivated by uncontrollable instincts cannot believe that they create their reality and control their health. To make the subconscious a friend, it is necessary to give up the pretense of subconscious motivation and to take full responsibility for your life and actions.

There is a constant interaction between the conscious and the subconscious mind. The subconscious is truly the well of creativity, but it can run dry if it is too tightly lidded by a critical ego that will not honor it. If you blame the subconscious for what is programmed or stored in it, you are denying your own power and freedom of choice. If you approach the subconscious with intent and purpose, it can help you live with elegance and inspiration rather than struggle and illness.

You can befriend your subconscious at any time; you do not need professional help to allow your life to become more healthy and abundant. One of the keys to working effectively with your subconscious is to deal with it as you would a helpful friend. If you want something from a friend, you have to know specifically what you want. When you go over to a friend's home and ask him for a garden tool, you have to know specifically what you want so he can search for it in the right place.

The subconscious responds best to pictures, so if there is something that you want to bring into your life, it is wise to create a picture of it and hold that picture in your mind. The subconscious will then help to bring it into your life in the easiest, most elegant way, without struggle or hardship to anyone involved.

The Use of Imagery in Healing

Images of an illness help us to understand the emotional, mental and spiritual messages of conflict symbolized by it. For instance, Cecillia's image of her candidiasis as a heavy metal bell without a ringer told her that she had hardened herself, making herself tough and expressionless. In her hard, defensive posture, Cecillia had not allowed herself to express her feelings. In childhood, she had constructed a hard shield to protect herself against what she had been taught was a fearful world, making it impossible for her to process and express her feelings. Unfortunately, she passed this attitude on to her children who were also developing symptoms of candidiasis.

An image is an inner picture of your experience–the feelings, thoughts, and messages, and what you see, hear, feel, smell and taste. Some people respond more to images of feeling than those of sight. Images become the language of the subconscious, giving you an inner picture of what is happening to both your body and your mind. Imagery is the best way to contact your deep inner self, and adding relaxing music enhances this process.

A healing image is a response to the image of illness at not just a physical level, but at an emotional, mental and spiritual level as well. It answers the message of an illness by responding to what is missing or needed to resolve a conflict. To heal herself, Cecillia had to become less hard and more expressive. She had to be willing to become as clear and as vulnerable as a crystal bell. She had to give herself permission to express her emotions and thoughts. Cecillia had to believe that she was as beautiful in her expression as that crystal bell.

A healing image suggests mental and emotional attitudes needed for healing to occur. Jane had a constriction in her throat that often made it difficult for her to speak. To loosen this constriction, Jane went into her subconscious and was given the image of a braided rope of flowers that she could unbraid. This rope represented the fears of her father and ex-husband that prevented her from expressing herself freely. The image of the rope of flowers showed her that she was in control of her fears and that she needed to face them. I suggested she use this healing image on a regular basis. Also, whenever she felt unable to speak, Jane could use this image to open up her throat and give herself permission to express herself.

I am very sensitive to images of sound and sight, and also have had conflicts over self-expression which manifested themselves in my hypothyroidism. While writing this book, I asked for a healing image to help me have the courage to succeed in the writing and in healing myself. In meditation, I was given the image of a conch shell. I considered this image as a gift from my Higher Self, with a special, magical meaning to me. I associate a conch shell with living magically–to listening and responding to messages from the sea of the subconscious and higher consciousness. Ten years before, while I was on the Island of Kauai, Hawaii, I would go early every morning to meditate in a special garden. And every morning I would hear the sound of a conch shell as I came into the garden. At first I thought this was the way the hotels nearby woke their guests. Then I realized that this was a message for me, because I was receptive and open in this garden.

The night after I received the conch shell in meditation, I woke to the low moaning sound of a conch shell. I was literally "conched" awake to the potential of living in balance, without struggle. Not only was this an inner image, but I began being confronted synchronistically with this image again and again in my outer reality. This image appeared in neighbors' yards and on the cover of the book in which my poems recently appeared. (My friends in Alaska had selected the image of the conch shell for the cover of the poetry book *Whispered Secrets* without consulting me.) Whenever this image appeared, it reminded me that I was not alone, and that if I listened and responded, I would find my success and healing.

The more holistic your healing meditation is, the more effective it will be. If you address the healing of one organ or symptom, it will be healed temporarily but the illness will probably reappear in that organ or another related one if you do not address the underlying conflict the illness symbolizes.

Joan had a cancerous tumor in her liver and stomach area. While she was in hospital isolation during chemotherapy, her spleen also became enlarged and affected. We began to see how much her habit of worrying impacted the progress of her illness. The central conflict of her illness was anxiety that came from worry and controlling her feelings in an effort to be perfect. In Joan's family, feelings were considered improper, and only her mother (who had a nervous breakdown during Joan's adolescence) was allowed to express feelings, particularly those of anger.

Together, Joan and I created a healing meditation tape that she used regularly, which addressed both her diseased organs and also this conflict. The tape gave her permission to forgive herself and to let go of the burden of perfectionism, cynicism and self-criticism which was causing her to repress her feelings. It also encouraged her to express all her feelings as honestly and appropriately as possible, and helped her let go of the belief that she had to worry to keep things from going wrong. Although her prognosis was grave, her tumors continued to shrink as she gave herself permission to feel. Joan chose special music for her tape that she associated with a time in her life when she was loving, enthusiastic and hopeful, and it helped to draw out these feelings in her now.

Imagery directly affects the body by influencing heart rate, blood pressure, respiratory patterns, oxygen consumption, carbon dioxide elimination, brain-wave rhythms and patterns, and the hormonal and immune systems. Music also effects heart rate, blood pressure and brain-wave patterns, and helps to evoke imagery. For instance, by imagining your hands as heavy and warm, or as being near a hot fire, you can raise the temperature of your hands. As a side-effect of raising your hand temperature, you can also heal yourself of migraine headaches. Your body, through your subconscious, communicates through images. If you quiet yourself and then create an image of what you want to happen to your body, your body will make that image happen.

The image of an illness and its healing together suggest the central issues involved in an illness and the way these can be healed. While I was counseling a young woman named Mary, who had arthritis in her knees, she asked for an image of her self-image and its healing. Her self-image was that of a "molly" bolt in a wall, unable to move. Her new self-image was of a silver ring with roses on it to symbolize her need to open herself to love (the roses) and to a new sense of her wholeness (the silver ring).

Healing Imagery as Symbolic Communication with an Illness

To heal an illness, the imagery used responds to and answers the emotional, mental and spiritual needs symbolized by the illness. Issues of bitterness and anger are healed when there is an expression, release and forgiveness of the symbol behind a physical symptom. For instance, Irma told me that she could remember having chosen to create the fibroids in her uterus that she later chose to heal. These fibroids had grown so large that they needed to be removed in some way. Irma chose to work with imagery as her first option. These fibroids were to her a symbol of her frustrated creativity and represented the children she never had but still longed for. They also represented her bitterness and anger at her ex-husband whom she felt had used her sexually and prevented her from having the children she desired. Irma's healing process was to emotionally, mentally and spiritually release the conflicts for which she had created these fibroids in the first place. She had to release the anger and bitterness in her uterus, to nurture it instead, and to find other avenues of creativity satisfying to her.

When Irma explored the message of her fibroids, she found that it was related to feelings of martyrdom and of being unappreciated and unnoticed by others, especially by her ex-husband. There was a bitterness and anger in her uterus that resented being appreciated only for her body and not for her whole self. To heal this, she realized she had to value and nurture herself. The core of the issue seemed to lie in her seeking self-esteem from outside herself rather than from within.

To heal, this fibroid needed to be nurtured by her. Irma used the healing image of a bucket to mop up the fibroids. In going within to explore them, Irma knew they were not cancerous, a fact later confirmed medically. She used the healing image of her own loving, caring hands massaging the fibroids, forcing them out, and giving them the love she felt she had not received before. The fibroids also represented her feelings of being unwanted as a child. The healing of her fibroids depended on Irma releasing the payoff of self-pity and martyrdom that the fibroids represented, replacing them with the nurturing of self-love and esteem that was symbolized by her healing hands.

Imagery as the Link Between the Conscious and Subconscious

Imagery is the link between the body and the mind, the conscious and the subconscious. Imagery precedes thought and may initiate the thought process. Imagery also precedes action. Many of the skilled athletes who compete in the Olympic Games use imagery in preparation for their performances. The reason imagery is so effective in healing is that the autonomic nervous system responds to perceptions both real and imaginary.

Your autonomic nervous system makes no distinction between imagery and reality. Imagine yourself in front of your refrigerator, reaching in for a lemon, slicing it and then placing it to your lips. Your body will respond by salivating and puckering in the same way you would if you were actually tasting a lemon. Imagery uses inner senses that correspond to your outer ones. There is no right way to image. If you do not visualize well, you can get just as much benefit from imagery by "seeing with your heart," participating fully by using your feelings.

Healing with imagery is basically imagining the sickness getting well. You visualize the problem and gradually alter it–sensing it get better all the time and your body being transformed to good health. To do this, you can use either symbolic or realistic healing images. A symbolic method of healing would be to see Vikings, Husky dogs or soldiers carrying away cancer cells; realistic methods of imagining would include imagining immune cells attacking the tumor and it gradually decreasing in size. Your body will respond effectively to either or both methods of healing. Do not limit or trick yourself with impatience. It takes time to reeducate the subconscious, so regular daily practice is extremely helpful. The more you become involved emotionally in this work, the more effective it will be.

The Function of the Subconscious Mind

The subconscious gathers all your beliefs, attitudes and experiences and puts them together harmoniously and consistently. All information that reaches you must pass through the filter of your subconscious. Only what fits the screen of your beliefs, experiences and attitudes will reach you.   The subconscious is a wonderful servant, perfectly fulfilling the commands it receives from your beliefs, whether they are destructive or constructive. If you are thinking and feeling, for instance, that you wish you could go back and do it all over again, or you wish you could start all over again, and this time do it right, your subconscious mind gathers this attitude and sends it to the cells of your body where they serve you by carrying out your message. If these messages to the body are destructive, they can lead to illnesses like cancer.

The subconscious stores all of your ideas, so it can inspire and help you deal with issues that seem to be blocking you, by offering creative solutions. The subconscious is the doorway to every aspect and dimension of personal existence. Through this doorway can come understanding and wisdom that can be helpful in allowing you to see a health problem or some other problem in a new way. One of the causes of illness is a narrowness of viewpoint that does not see creative possibilities and opportunities. This narrow viewpoint may harbor resentments and angers, and refuse to be grateful.

The subconscious is usually seen as a conservative force that locks us into our past and its beliefs, but it need not be if we focus our desire on becoming healthier people. Fear of the subconscious is often related to fear of facing who we really are. Beliefs are the raw materials from which our attitudes, our emotions and our material realities spring. What we believe sets the boundaries of what is possible for us. To recognize that your beliefs and attitudes

125

precede and create your body is the key to changing your life in a more healthy direction.

If you want to change the kind of body you have, you need to first change your beliefs and emotions. If, for instance, you hold the belief that "life is a struggle," and that you will only be worthy if you have a high-paying job, then these beliefs cause you to have a constantly competitive and striving attitude. This attitude may lead to heart disease or other stress related illnesses.

To heal yourself from a destructive belief system, it is necessary to seek some alternative belief system that will allow you to live your life with less stress to your body and mind. You can only change an experience of ill health by replacing the attitudes and beliefs from which this illness originates with healthier ones. You cannot just *remove* beliefs; your only option is whether to *replace* them or not, and what the replacement will be. This kind of self-exploration can begin with the process of asking yourself, "What kind of beliefs must I have to create the kind of reality I am now experiencing?" If you have a stomach ulcer, you can ask about the beliefs that could have caused you to create the kind of reality that would cause a stomach ulcer.

Your subconscious mind is constantly interacting with your conscious mind, accepting whatever beliefs you give it–whether they are hopeful or not. If you choose to be hopeful and not to die of cancer, for instance, you begin to expect health and to do those things that free you of despair. Your conscious choices affect the chemistry of your body through your subconscious mind, which in turn influences your glandular and immune systems.

The Discipline of Healing Using the Subconscious

Imagery is most effective if it is directed at not just the physical symptom, but the mental, emotional and spiritual aspects of your life that created it. If I were to create imagery and music tapes for you, I would use music and imagery that helps you become more emotionally involved in your healing. Music is a co-therapist in a healing tape or meditation because it helps you to feel more. To this end, music that you love is chosen, within certain guidelines. The music should be quiet and instrumental to promote meditation and to prevent distraction. Also, it should match your emotional healing need. For instance, if you are experiencing asthma, and the central conflict of asthma is grief, you would select not only music that touches you but music that would allow you to grieve.

To create a healing tape or meditation for yourself or another, you can begin with the eight steps mentioned in Simontons' book *Getting Well Again*. These steps are only a beginning to what can be a fully healing experience. Add to these steps specific suggestions concerning the resolution of the illness conflict.

For instance, if you are healing heart disease, make suggestions directed to healing the characteristics of a Type A life style. Such suggestions would counteract a tendency to be quick to anger, to rush, and to be judgemental of oneself and others. These would encourage inner values such as honesty and integrity as the basis of self-esteem. If you are healing cancer, encourage the honest and appropriate expression of feeling necessary to counteract Type C behavior. The use of music is especially useful in encouraging this emotional involvement.

The Simontons did a controlled study on the difference between a group of cancer patients who used imagery in the healing of their cancer and those who did not. Both groups were receiving conventional medical treatment, and were considered medically incurable. Those who used imagery lived twice as long as those who did not. We can wonder and ask how much more successful the Simontons' work with imagery would have been if their healing process had been a holistic one.

Becoming emotionally involved in your healing will be fostered by doing your healing meditation in a consistent way. The ideal attitude is to see the meditation as a gift of self-healing, not as a stern discipline. Begin with learning how to relax and to use your receptive will. A healing visualization gives your body the command to heal after your mind and body have become quieted.

Healing will not result if you meditate without commitment or emotional involvement. Twenty minutes of an emotionally distracted meditation is not enough to change your body's chemistry. To avoid distraction, you may need to create your own special healing tape, or to seek some help. The more emotionally and imaginatively involved you are, the more effective you will be in using healing imagery.

Patti, a friend, had a plantar wart on her foot that would have required a painful operation to remove. Instead, her physician recommended that she use regular periods of visualization. Several times a day, Patti relaxed and visualized the wart as an octopus whose tentacles she saw being cut and pulled out of her foot. Within weeks the wart was entirely gone. To heal an illness it is necessary to use disciplined relaxation and quiet meditation regularly. This means taking the same time in the same place for meditation each day, preferably in the morning when you have just awakened. By using the same time and place each day, your subconscious gains a sense of security.

Your subconscious mind can be viewed as a computer room, an underground labyrinth, a huge library or a vast room containing information inside little boxes. To find the information you want from the subconscious, it is helpful to have keys to open it such as music, sounds or smells, and access points–objects such as a crystal or piece of jewelry. To use the subconscious mind, you can appeal to its friendly side by approaching it either as a loving person or as a seeker who is attempting to excel and become more of whom you were meant to be. To get the information you want, you have to know what it is you want and you need to find an access point–a personally symbolic object or image–to gain this information.

For instance, you can go into the subconscious to examine a disease process and to discover its hidden message. You do so with the recognition that this message, though unknown to your conscious mind, is related to processes of your mind with which you are very familiar. Visualization in meditation helps to center the subconscious mind, to focus your attention, and to allow inner guidance to come through. It helps to speak to your higher self and to write down the answers you receive. The process of writing helps you become focused and allows a greater flow of communication. When I am counseling someone, I suggest that he or she keep a journal in which to record dreams and insights.

Allowing the Subconscious to Balance You Through Intuition

The subconscious is a feminine energy that transcends reason and that has to be approached with the receptivity of your feminine side. To be able to work with your subconscious mind as a friend, you have to call on that part of yourself which is feminine (regardless, of course, of your gender). This part of yourself opens you to inner guidance and intuition. To have this kind of feminine openness and receptivity, it is necessary to give up the fear of loss of control and to accept a higher level of freedom. The use of your intuition helps you overcome a tendency to struggle unnecessarily.

Instead of the ego's need for control, struggle and conflict, the subconscious can help us live and work with an elegance, and ease that is not possible if we rely on the ego alone. Barry Neil Kaufman, in his autobiography, *A Sense of Warning*, not only got rid of his migraine headaches by befriending and using his subconscious mind, he also became very intuitive and creative in his graphic design business. Those projects that had taken great struggle and effort before came easily and were finished with much more creative energy and skill than was possible while he relied on ego control alone. On several occasions, Kaufman's daughter Rachel was in danger. By following his intuition, Kaufman was able to help her when she needed him. On one occasion he prevented her from choking; on another, he was able to stop her from being run over by a runaway horse and carriage.

Overcoming the Fear of the Subconscious

To befriend the subconscious, it is necessary to get beyond the fears commonly associated with it. These fears come from our programming from families, religions and schools that emphasize the power of the conscious mind while devaluing the creativity of the subconscious. The subconscious creative process is often cheapened by calling its activities daydreaming or fantasizing.

The attitude with which you approach the subconscious is a crucial one. If you approach the subconscious with fear, a friendly and helpful relationship is unlikely. If, however, you use the subconscious as a co-creator and friend, you can reach into it with an honest sense of power and expectation. When the subconscious is considered a friend, there is no longer that fear that if you enter it, you might find that you are an evil person, or that monsters, snakes and spiders might overcome you.

You would not blame or fear your computer for the programs you store in it, but many of us fear and blame our subconscious minds for what we store there. The fear of the subconscious originates in the false belief that there are instincts and uncontrollable urges buried in it that determine our behavior. This belief originated in Freudian psychology and it did describe many of the sick individuals of his time. We no longer live in the late 19th century; we can now create our lives through our conscious and higher conscious minds.

We can befriend the subconscious by reprogramming the destructive programs that have produced illness and unhappiness for us. If we could not control the subconscious mind and through it our bodies, there would be no free will and no reason for hope. The subconscious mind can be seen as a filter through which the outside world tries to reach us. If that filter is cluttered with destructive beliefs and feelings, the outside world, no matter how loving and beautiful, can not reach us. Someone can walk up to you and say sincerely, "I like you. I want to be your friend." If you are holding the feeling "Don't trust people, they will only use you," then that sincere message of friendship will not be accepted; it will not get through the dirty filter of your subconscious mind. Part of human development is clearing away beliefs that are destructive to our health.

Fear of the subconscious mind often originates with parents who do not want us to be free-spirited. Our parents do not want us to go off in flights of fancy because they mistakenly believe they are preparing us to be better people by stifling our creativity. Parents very often discourage imaginary friends and imaginative activities in young children. If a child wishes to play by him- or herself, parents are sometimes alarmed, thinking their child will be unpopular or unable to adjust to the outside world and its demands. Sometimes parents portray the subconscious as a bogey man that will reach out and grab a child; the child hears this and closes off the inner world of creativity and intuition.

Public education also discourages the use of the subconscious mind. Teachers usually expect their students to pay attention. When a child daydreams or becomes absorbed in his or her own inner worlds, the teacher labels that child as a discipline problem. As a result, school often seems dull, negative, depressing and boring to a creative child. The message often taught to children is to not rely on their subconscious minds and their creative abilities, but on the authority of teachers and books. What this traditional education denies is the playfulness and receptivity to the subconscious that is always present whenever creative ideas come forth.

Modern psychology is another source of fear of the subconscious; it maintains that the subconscious is a scary realm that can only be faced with professional help. Many religions discourage the use of the subconscious by saying it is the work of the devil, and that we should fear the evil that is within us. Some metaphysical teachings also foster a fear of the subconscious through dwelling on dark forces that will get you if you are not careful to protect yourself and to control your psychic explorations.

The most common source of fear of the subconscious, though, is the negative ego. It tells us to stay away from the subconscious, because the ego has control of everything and does not wish to give that up. It reassures us that it can take care of us and that everything is fine without the help of the subconscious mind. The negative ego can limit not only our creativity, but our spiritual and human potential. It will not help us overcome an illness, because it is the source of that illness. The negative ego must be denied and rejected if we are to listen to and answer the hidden messages of an illness.

One of the fears we have about the subconscious mind is that within it are all the ugly thoughts, fears and terrible things we have done, so it is better not to explore that area. Many people feel the subconscious is like Pandora's box, that if we open it all kinds of ugly, awful things will be released into the world. The risk that the contents might be awful and ugly is perhaps the greatest fear we have of the subconscious.

Another fear we have of the subconscious is that it does not operate logically or rationally, so we cannot know how it will behave. The subconscious also stores our motivations and intentions, so to the extent we are hiding from our emotions, motivations and intentions, we will avoid facing what is within the subconscious. Another fear related to the subconscious is that of a loss of control, because we cannot control its creative process with logic and reason.

Many people fear the subconscious because within it are stored our emotions. To the extent that we are afraid of the intensity of our emotions, we fear our subconscious minds. But the subconscious mind does not create these emotions, it merely stores them for us when we refuse to process and release them. Many people hold beliefs that will not allow them to deal with their emotions.

All of these fears are actually fairly easy to resolve. While we do not know what the subconscious mind will bring us, we can and do know how we can effectively approach and work with it. The subconscious can help us release and process the emotions that are held in our bodies and minds, so we can live more healthy lives. The subconscious is the servant of every person and shows no favors. It is the great equalizer; it gives creative ideas and help to whoever uses it, no matter their status or experience.

Chapter Seven

Emotions and Illness

There is an emotional conflict behind every illness. If we reach and resolve the emotional root of an illness, we can heal it. The origin of most illnesses is suppressed or repressed anger, hurt, self-hatred or refusal to love. Our bodies are the garbage dumps for our unresolved feelings. Our feelings do not disappear just because we deny or ignore them. If we do not express anger, fear or shame, they are expressed in our bodies, stuffed in our backs, arms, legs or in some internal organ.

To heal, we need to *feel* these emotions, *resolve them on an emotional intuitive level* and then *forgive* them. It is not enough to merely intellectually understand our pain or to feel it only. We need to both feel and know its meaning in order to release stuffed or denied emotions. Expressing an emotion such as anger does not resolve it. True healing requires that we recognize and give up the payoff that we are taking; in the case of anger that would usually be self-righteousness.

The connection between emotions and bodily reactions is difficult to study in traditional scientific ways. However, healers have always been aware of the interaction between our bodies and emotions. Galen, a physician in the second century A.D., attributed cancer to a melancholy disposition. Medieval physicians tried to relate certain illnesses to particular mental dispositions such as phlegmatic, sanguine or lacking in bile. Only a century ago, physicians were much more aware of the interaction of emotional states and illness than most physicians are today. Sr. James Paget, a physician of that time, noted such a frequency of cases where hopelessness and despair were followed by the development of a malignant cancer that he saw a direct relationship between the mental depression and the development of the subsequent malignancy.

The Symbolic Expression of Emotions such as Anger and Hurt

Repressed anger and hurt do not lay dormant in us; they destroy us and affect those around us. Poor health often represents an oozing out through the body of unexpressed emotions–tucked away love, shame, anger, fear, resentment and hate. If we do not release these emotions, they become destructive to our bodies. Hurt often settles in our backs and anger gets put in some internal organ or in an arm or leg. Anger, shame and hurt that are unexpressed are probably the biggest sources of illness.

We all have the choice to handle emotions such as hurt, anger or shame cleanly or to stuff them. If we choose to repress emotions instead of processing them, our bodies suffer. Many people do not want to be responsible for their emotions and deny or suppress them. Meanwhile these emotions run their lives and make them ill. To release emotions such as anger or hurt appropriately, you express these feelings honestly to yourself or others. This could be done by talking to the person involved, through writing hate letters, talking it out to a friend or counselor, talking to yourself in the mirror, etc. Whatever the method, then forgive yourself and others involved.

This means you do not hold on to these emotions to punish others or yourself, but face them responsibly and cleanly. Anger that is denied and unexpressed can destroy you in the form of cancer. I once counseled a woman named Joyce who had cancer throughout her body. Joyce had been in psychotherapy with others for some time, but had had little success in releasing her angry feelings. She was angry at her father, husband and daughter; she rationalized and felt justified in her anger. When I asked for a healing image to help her release her anger, we were given the image of a large cauldron or pot. During relaxation, I asked Joyce to identify those places on her body where she held her anger. She described these places in terms of color and shape; for instance, she told me that there was a large black anger around her solar plexus and a small red anger at her heart. Then I asked her to visualize and enter a deep forest and to find a clearing. In the middle of this clearing was a large cauldron cooking on a fire.

Beginning at her feet, Joyce then brought to this cauldron one by one those places upon her body where she held anger. Joyce visualized these centers of anger in terms of shapes and colors. She watched these slowly dissolving in the cauldron and at times asked for help to allow this anger to be released. Joyce had trouble releasing the anger at her throat. I told her to bring a blue healing light with her to help her heal this anger. Shortly after this session, Joyce's cancer went into remission.

The Destructiveness of Shame

Toxic shame has a devastating effect upon the body, because it damages the chemical balance in your mind and body; these chemical reactions shred and weaken your immune system. Toxic shame expresses itself as not only the feeling that you have done things that are bad or wrong, but that *you are* bad and wrong. Toxic shame can originate in emotional, mental and sexual abuse from either subhuman or superhuman parents. Subhuman parents are emotionally, mentally, or physically abusive. Superhuman parents abuse by expecting children to be perfect, better than others, to prove their own superiority.

If you are a perfectionist, you are always going to feel like a failure and be anxious. That feeling will make you tired. As you grow older and your immune system is less resilient, your body reflects that tiredness. To survive an overwhelming childhood shame, many people agreed upon contracts with the offending person, such as a mother or father. There are several kinds of shame- based contracts that can be recognized, owned, forgiven and released. Shame-based contracts keep the offender alive and prevent you from being yourself.

One kind of shame-based contract is that which clones the offender by being like him or her in as many ways as possible such as in your choice of profession. You then live to get their approval by thinking and acting in ways they would approve. Some try to be an extension of what the offender wished they could have been such as the lawyer or cheerleader. If your parents were unfeeling, you may have learned to "not feel" as a way of coping with the pain that was there; this not feeling may have been following their example or may have been a defense against their abuse. In any case, a contract to "not feel" is destructive to your immune system and can lead to the Type C behavior pattern that is related to illnesses such as arthritis, cancer and chronic fatigue syndrome.

Another kind of shame-based contract is that in which one is the exact opposite of the offender. If he was subhuman, you are perfect or superhuman. If she was an awful wife and mother, you will be a superwife and mother. The trouble with a opposition contract is that when you are always reacting to the offender, you are never yourself. You become merely the other side of the coin... which is still the same coin.

One type of contract that directly affects the body is that of having a psychic leak in which the energy of the offender actually drains your own. Diseases and physical symptoms such as chronic fatigue syndrome, cancer, candidiasis, left-side migraine head-aches, lower back pain, knee and neck pains are often related to psychic leaks from taking on other people's burdens and their draining your energy. You agree to always be there for them and to live your life for them. In contracts involving psychic leaks, the offender or his surrogates actually drain your psychic energy and thus weaken you and your immune system.

In her book *The Type C Connection*, Temoshok asks whether a melanoma could be localized in an area of the body where a psychic tension had gathered from an unresolved trauma. She had two patients with melanomas in places on their bodies that were not overexposed to the sun, the usual explanation given for melanoma.

Marilyn had a melanoma on the big toe of her left foot, and had just experienced a stressful time in her life in which she felt responsible for the care of a gravely ill mother who was suffering from the complications of diabetes. Marilyn had apparently contracted to do anything to help and please her mother. Her mother had gangrene develop on a toe of her left foot and eventually had to have this toe, and then her entire left leg amputated. Through this all, Marilyn sacrificed herself ceaselessly to care for her mother. One explanation could be that Marilyn had a psychic leak contract to be an extension of her mother. This may have manifested itself as a melanoma on the same place in which her mother's gangrene developed. This contract also is related to left side/right brain conflicts with her feminine or mother's energy.

Another example Temoshok gave was that of Wendy, a young woman who developed a melanoma within the folds of her vagina, a rare occurrence. This shy young woman had a strict Catholic upbringing and sex was considered a hush-hush topic in her family. As a girl, Wendy had been raped by her great uncle. She had not told anyone, but had kept her shame and feelings secret. She was afraid of being accused of encouraging her uncle and of being rejected by her family. This repressed conflict manifested itself as cancer in the place it originated.

Shame has to be released and processed in a different way than anger. Unlike anger, toxic shame is not yours. It was dumped upon you–usually by some adult like a parent, uncle, teacher or minister. One way to process it is to have it lifted or taken from your heart or shoulders by your Higher Self. Another way is to give it in meditation back to the offender who dumped it upon you–the mother or uncle who abused you and shamed you by her or his shame.

It is often necessary to ask for spiritual help to lift the last residues of that shame from your heart and mind. In this process, you do not change the offender, but you do change how you reacted to this offense–what you said or did or what others such as protectors or helpers did to protect you from it. If this offense happened while you were a child or young adult, recognize that you did not know how to defend yourself against it. As a child, you were not bad. The adult person involved, however, was responsible and needs to be given back the shame that was dumped on you. Forgive yourself and forgive the offender. You need not forget what abusive thing was done to you, but you need to forgive why it was done. It sometimes helps to forgive by recalling similar incidents when you too shamed others, without recognizing the full impact of what you were doing.

Refusal to Feel Grief, and John's Asthma

In order for life to flow more smoothly, you can learn to balance both the feminine and masculine energies–to trust your inner guidance and act on the intuitions and feelings of your feminine side as well as to use your assertive, active masculine energies. Many of the solutions to health problems will be found in working with the feminine energies of imagination, emotion and desire. I once counseled a man named John who had chronic asthma, severe enough to cause him to be hospitalized occasionally. The doctors told him there was no solution to his asthma, other than to take medication to relieve his symptoms.

The night before John came to see me, I had a dream in which I was a welfare officer in the office to which a man like John came with his family to make a complaint. John sat in front of his father and they both complained of injustices done to them. Meanwhile, his sister acted crazily and went about the office dumping over wastepaper baskets. In the dream, my way of helping the family was to give his sister a white robe. The dream was a clue that the way to help John was to make his feminine energy white or holy

138

again because he viewed it as crazy and thus he feared and discredited it.

As I worked with John using relaxation, imagery and music, I helped him begin to dream, imagine and honor his feminine side. In his imagery, John saw that the left side of himself was dead or vacant. John was unable to be truly creative, spiritual and emotional without revaluing this side of himself. He had allowed his wife to express the emotions for his family. John also saw how he had tried to live his father's life rather than his own, because of his fear that he would be crazy or destructive if he allowed his feminine side to emerge. He had deep grief over his loss of integrity. When he allowed himself to grieve, to recognize his many talents, and to allow his feminine energies to come forth, his health improved dramatically. Two years after I worked with him, he had no symptoms of asthma.

The Symbolic Expression of Anger

Poor health often represents an oozing out through the body of unexpressed emotions–tucked away love, anger, fear, resentment and hate. Those repressed emotions can express themselves in arthritis, ulcers, heart disease, cancer and other illnesses. The illnesses of old age often represent a release of stuffed emotions, so an elderly person will not take them with him or her in death.

Repressed anger can express itself in a tumor or growth; it can also express itself in a rigidity of body that denies the anger's existence. Suppressed and unexpressed anger is lethal; it does not lay dormant within us, it destroys us and those around us. We all have the choice to handle our anger cleanly or to stuff it down inside and let it seep out in illness or in other subversive ways. Cara, a woman who had chronic arthritis, showed no emotional response in traditional psychotherapy for a year. When she finally broke down her defenses during a counseling session with a therapist, because her husband had forgotten her birthday, she was furious for the first time in her life. This outrage was followed by a total disappearance of her symptoms–pain, joint swelling, fatigue and morning stiffness. (Arehart-Treichel, 1980)

As a result of her psychotherapy, another rheumatoid patient, Mabel, vented her pent up resentment against her husband by hitting him over the head with a chair. Her husband had to get medical care, but Mabel felt fantastic. Her rheumatoid symptoms subsided dramatically and remained quiescent for many weeks. Although there are more appropriate ways of expressing anger than assaulting your spouse, these examples still show the relationship of suppressed anger to the creation of arthritis.

All anger gets processed either through our bodies as illness or cleanly through other forms of expression. Only we decide how to process our anger. Many health problems can be related to repressed or suppressed anger. Anger expressed cleanly and appropriately can be a valuable force to free oneself and others from injustice, oppression and domination. Anger can be seen as the first step in a process of transformation that is sometimes necessary before one can reach inner peace and equilibrium.

The recognition and expression of anger has proven to be an effective way to heal many serious illnesses. A psychologist at Johns Hopkins Medical School recently surveyed 35 breast cancer patients. He found that women who expressed anger not only toward their disease but toward their physicians lived longer and had a better chance of recovery than those who were pleasant and cooperative. In the early 1970s, long-living heart attack patients were compared to those who did not survive. The former were found to be much less anxious and depressed than the latter. They also expressed immense satisfaction and gratitude for being able to do things they did not expect to be able to do. Anger can be processed in a clean, honest and appropriate way that releases it or in a dirty way that suppresses and represses it, and then holds it within the body.

Anger has secondary effects that some people value as well. Some of us retain our anger because we have the mistaken notion that an angry person is a powerful person. This false belief comes from a misunderstanding of the nature of power. Real power is not domination of others. Some people use anger as a way of making themselves feel alive when they feel powerless. When anger is held and unexpressed, it can be the major fuel for the negative ego. When there is suppressed anger, instead of the ego carrying messages of what is happening around it, it assumes that a simple act such as spilling a glass of milk was done deliberately to humiliate or hurt. Anger inflates the negative ego and alienates us from life, if not expressed appropriately and honestly.

Fear, Anger, and Jack's Lower Back Pain

When anger and fear are present with lower back pain, they are often related to economic worries and insecurities. Jack had a congenital imbalance in which his pelvis was tilted forward, placing pressure on his nerves. This condition was especially painful during times of internal conflict and stress. Imbalances related to family relationships are often expressed in deformities of the bones or in problems with the blood. When Jack focused on his lower back pain, he got the image of logs burning on a fire. One of the logs was cracked and broken. Jack felt pulled in two different directions. The fire in his lower back, he knew, represented his rage at being pulled in two directions and feeling unable to focus upon what he really desired to learn and be. In meditation, we asked what was pulling him forward. The answer was, "The need to understand." Pulling him backward was a fear of failure, humiliation, criticism and financial worries. Jack was a perfectionist who constantly tried to keep up with his professional field.

What he really wanted to learn and be was a liberal, progressive lawyer. Instead, he was pulled backward by the fear that he would not survive and would be destitute if he dared to be a nonconformist. He recalled conversations at the dinner table when he was told as a child that he would be a penniless vagrant if he did not stop fooling around and decide to amount to something. The conflict in his back was symbolic of being pulled in two ways by fear and a desire to grow. He felt he did not have a secure base and did not know enough. His back pain began in college when he was studying constantly.

There were pressures on Jack from his family and society to follow the safe, secure, traditional route of his profession, but he was pulled to follow his passions and intuitions. His heart's desire was to explore nontraditional ways of being a lawyer, helping the poor and underprivileged. He felt enraged at feeling unsupported and living a life not his own. Occasionally, he got symptoms of asthma and allergies that expressed his mourning for living a life that was repugnant to him. His father was a traditional lawyer; it grieved Jack to feel he was not living his unique patterns, but was choosing the safe way of his father.

Through Guided Imagery and Music, Jack asked the inner wisdom of his higher conscious mind for something to put out this fire. The answer was to learn what he wanted to learn, and to master his fears about failure, humiliation, criticism and survival. Jack gradually began to permit himself to follow his passions and to express his uniqueness. He affirmed that his inner passion was essential to his success. He began to trust his intuitions more and to take more risks. Jack had to face his tendency to be a perfectionist. He also had to stop taking the payoffs of clinging to the past, and avoiding taking responsibility for his life. By not taking risks, he might feel more secure, but the price he paid was giving up his uniqueness and his dreams.

Emotional Honesty

"Your health is bound to be affected," wrote Boris Pasternak in *Doctor Zhivago*, "if, day after day, you say the opposite of what you feel, if you grovel before what you dislike and rejoice at what brings you nothing but misfortune. Our nervous system is not just a fiction, it's part of our physical body, and our soul exists in space and is inside us, like teeth in our mouth. It can't be forever violated with impunity."

The effects of suppressing emotions and living with dishonesty are seen in the health of those married to alcoholics. The occurrence of cancer among the spouses of alcoholics is significantly higher than in marriages without an alcoholic spouse. To live with an alcoholic means that you are likely to experience the anger of dealing with a person who refuses to be responsible for his own actions. If this anger at the alcoholic is not expressed appropriately and honestly, it may find expression in malignancy. Old destructive codependent relationships need to be recognized, forgiven and released. The spouse of an alcoholic often plays the role of enabler, martyr or savior to the alcoholic while a cauldron of anger builds within.

Better to face the anger, express it, and make the changes necessary for your healing. In a relaxed state of body and mind, new perspectives on a situation or illness can be imagined. The subconscious, which stores all of our emotions, can be tapped so these can be released. Sometimes a good cry or an appropriate release of anger can do wonders to heal us.

Depression and the Anger Underlying Margery's Arthritis

Many illnesses begin with some form of repressed anger that first has to be recognized and then released. Guilt represents the anger you feel you have no right to express. Depression is the anger for which you feel you will get into trouble if you express it; it is also a reaction to a sudden change. When you feel depressed it is wise to identify the source. You can ask yourself if there is anger in your life, if you will get in trouble if you express it, or has there been a sudden change in your life. In depression, you feel helpless and inert–unable to move or act. Depression is common in women who feel powerless to express their anger, especially toward husbands or family members whose love and support would be threatened if they expressed that anger.

Before the depression or guilt underlying an illness can be released, it is necessary to transform that depression or guilt into the anger underlying it. Margery had a severe form of rheumatoid arthritis that had been treated unsuccessfully. This illness so limited her freedom and activities that even her sexual life was affected. The medication she was given for her arthritis caused her to gain much weight, making her even more depressed. Margery felt she was becoming physically unattractive to her husband. Then Margery made an unsuccessful suicide attempt; she took an overdose of Elavil, an antidepressant which had been prescribed to her. Margery was hospitalized and given psychiatric help, and she was filled with rage about her life.

Her arthritic symptoms began three years before, shortly after she felt betrayed by another woman who had taken over the business she and her husband had hoped to run. Margery did not trust people, especially men. She had married young and become an alcoholic. It was a pattern within her life to be sweet, beautiful, and to fail to process the anger and hurt she felt. Margery was recovering from alcoholism before her outbreak of arthritis. Her childhood was an unhappy one; she felt used and abused by her parents.

To understand the symbolic message of Margery's illness, it is necessary to look specifically at what was happening to her body. Her autoimmune system was attacking all the joints in her body and she was in great pain. One of the factors that seems to be related to arthritis is a failure of the body to eliminate toxins; they build up in the body and the liver and kidneys fail to filter them out. Similarly, in her mental, emotional and spiritual life there was a refusal to let go of and express her angers and fears concerning her relationships. Margery's history of alcoholism speaks of a long history of inability to process destructive emotions and thoughts. Margery was imbalanced because her depression hid a rage that she thought would cause rejection from her husband if she expressed it.

Margery saw herself as a victim of life and her past, viewing both with little satisfaction. The one avenue of satisfaction she had–her intimacy with her husband–seemed to be threatened. During the first three days Margery was in the hospital, while the drug Elavil was being purged from her body, Margery's arthritic symptoms disappeared. During those days, Margery could again move her legs and arms without pain. These days of symptom-free health point out the importance of eliminating toxins, both mental and physical.

During the days Margery spent in the hospital, she was encouraged to express her emotions and the reasons behind her suicide attempt. To heal her arthritis and the depression associated with it, Margery had to face her tendency to give up her power, blame others, and suppress her anger when things did not go as she wanted them to go. She felt great fear that she would lose the love of her husband as her body became disfigured, fat, and immobilized by pain and illness. There was also anger from feeling powerless against the force of her illness. Healing was possible for Margery only when she was able to process and release the anger and fear she felt; these unprocessed emotions were symbolized by the inability of her body to release toxins and to move forward freely.

Depression can be compared to a pressure cooker in which many, many angers have been repressed until the pressure builds until one feels helpless to move or to act. Many illnesses are often preceded by depression, which is a signal to the immune system to either shut down and stop defending the body, or to defend the body excessively. Such an overactive immune system is apparent in the case of autoimmune diseases. It is significant that rheumatoid arthritis is predominantly a women's disease, since women more often than men feel compelled to inhibit anger if they want to be loved and provided for.

Cancer and heart disease are among the many diseases likely to be preceded by depression. The anger that lies behind cancer is often a despair that does not immobilize, but does affect, the immune system by pervading the body with a sense of hopelessness.

Before you can release the anger that is depression, you must honestly face the burden of all the seemingly insignificant angers that accumulated until you became unable to move under the combined weight of them. One example would be an instance of being treated with indifference or disrespect by someone important to you. There are many images that can be used to release these built up pressures. One is that of a pressure cooker slowly releasing steam; watch it hiss and disperse around the room. Another helpful image is placing a heavy bag of sand on your body and then cutting it, slowly watching the sand fall upon the floor until there is only a handful left. Then fling it out the door or a window, releasing your angers with it.

Depression is always built up anger that we need to honestly face with the belief that there are many solutions to change any situation. After someone deals with the pressure of stored hurts and angers, he or she can deal more directly with the real anger underneath. Several possible ways that we can express anger appropriately without hurting anyone are to act it out in meditation, to talk it out with a friend, to speak out your true feelings to a mirror, or to write them out in a letter that is later burned.

Why We Suppress Anger

There are numerous social beliefs that, if accepted, prevent people from honestly recognizing and expressing their anger. Our culture is ambivalent about anger. We are encouraged to feel, but not to express these feelings, especially if they are intense. On one hand, we are told that it is important to our mental health to release anger, but we are also taught that it is unfeminine, unmasculine, unspiritual or otherwise not very nice to do so. Many people are taught to not express their anger in our society, as much by example as by words. Parents who suppress their anger teach their children to follow their example.

Parts of traditional masculine and feminine programming are the beliefs that teach us to suppress anger. The way to be a man, little boys are taught, is to never express your emotions, to suppress your anger, and to be cool headed. Women are supposed to be sweet and to never get angry; angry or aggressive women are considered bitches. Men are given more freedom to express their anger than women, but if they continue to be angry they are considered untrustworthy and unstable.

Our religious traditions teach us to rise above, suppress and deny anger, and to love everyone. The problem is when you are angry at someone and try to love them; you cannot do it. Between each of us is an energy field that, if filled with anger, cannot help being felt for what it is–a conflict hidden behind a front.

Your continued good health demands that you express and resolve anger cleanly, without harm to yourself or others. Anger is a human emotion that is not negative unless it is suppressed or repressed. Often it is not appropriate to express anger directly to another person involved, as this would set you up to take one of the payoffs such as self-pity or self-righteousness. Other ways of expressing your anger can be appropriately used at such times. Failing to express and release your anger, which can then lead to repressing or stuffing it, is the fuel that justifies judgemental feelings of either being better than or worse than those around us. These judgements separate us from others, and worse, separate us from our sense of unity with all things.

Fear and Sharon's Chronic Diarrhea and Agoraphobia

Fear is important to understand in relation to health, because of the effect it has on the body in times of stress. We all experience fear to some degree; those who face this fear with courage are able to succeed and remain healthy. When you are controlled by fear, you are paralyzed and powerless; you cannot react to the demands placed upon you. Fear locks you into old patterns and causes you to try to relive the past.

Sharon, a woman I once counseled, could not go out in public places without experiencing acute anxiety and diarrhea. As a result of these symptoms, Sharon had become a prisoner in her own home. When we explored what her diarrhea meant, we found out she was in a very uncomfortable situation at home, having been asked to care for her daughter's child. She wanted to be out of this situation, but was paralyzed with fear that she would lose her husband's love. Her own mother had been unable to hold a husband, so Sharon had decided she would please her husband and not make the same mistakes her mother had.

Sharon had never felt loved or cared for as a child, and much of our work together was spent healing the child within her, relieving its fears so Sharon could live her life. Through meditation, Sharon gave the child within her different parents and the love she needed, so this frightened child within her would stop running her life. This child would take over Sharon's life and become frightened in situations where Sharon felt she had no control. Sharon learned how to talk with and comfort her inner child when she had to visit hospitals or go out driving with her husband.

The payoff Sharon had to give up was clinging to the past while being a perfectionist. Sharon always compared herself to her mother and relived the past instead of forgiving and releasing it. She was so focused on being the opposite of her mother, she was failing to live her own life. Sharon learned to express her power and opinions to her husband in rehearsals of confrontations with him, using Guided Imagery and Music. She processed her fears as they arose and changed the subconscious programming that had allowed her child to run her life. Within six months, Sharon's diarrhea was gone and she was able to go out again in public places without fear.

Fear is part of every illness, but it is especially evident in the major killers–heart disease and cancer. A person with a Type A personality who develops heart disease is probably running scared. He or she lacks self-esteem and therefore must always be competing to receive outer validation as a source of self-esteem. Consequently, the bodies of Type A men and women are in a continual state of stress that leads to eventual heart damage.

Those who have cancer are also fearful; they are afraid that if they were what they truly desire to be, they would lose the love of others. Behind their desire to please and be loved, cancer patients have a fear of loneliness and rejection that denies their unique talents and desires. When you are paralyzed by a fear, you stop dreaming, and lose the vital energy that brings your dreams into reality and keeps you healthy.

To heal your fear, it is necessary to explore what you specifically fear and why. It is also necessary to recognize, own and release any payoffs such as avoidance, righteousness, self-pity and blame that you get from fear. You can begin to process fear by being alone for a few days to really explore what it is you fear. Write it out, talk it out to a mirror in specific detail, imagining specifically what the outcome of your fear would be. Write, "What really scares me is..." Be as honest as possible, adding to it over a three-day period, and then destroy your letter. When you are processing your fear, ask yourself if there is a message in it. What could the benefit of this fear be? What is the price you pay for giving in to fear?

Jane's Unforgiving and Suppressed Love

It takes courage to love again, especially to love someone who has hurt or betrayed you in the past. Love, like other emotions, is positive if expressed and negative if suppressed. More than anything else, a desire to have your pain validated by someone else blocks the healing process. The demand that your emotional wound be acknowledged by the person who inflicted it is an emotional blockage that stands in the way of healing. This forgiveness blockage is the most severe and common hindrance to genuine and complete healing.

Jane had a chronic, distended colon condition that was irritating and disabling. When we looked for the meaning of her illness,

Jane felt it was related to denying herself love and a fear of expressing her anger at her husband. Jane realized she had never completely forgiven him for a past extra-marital affair. Jane refused to love him or to receive his love fully because a part of her would not forgive him for having betrayed her while she was pregnant and in need of his support. The memory of his betrayal haunted her and kept her from trusting and committing herself to their relationship. Behind her refusal was a desire for him to acknowledge the pain he had caused her. Jane also felt that she did not deserve his love. She was angry at her husband for not supporting his family well, and at times sought a separation from him.

At the same time, she recognized that there was a love and caring between her and her husband that was sometimes genuine and dear. The retention of waste material in her body, Jane felt, symbolized her refusal to forgive her husband's past affair and to receive love from him. Stronger than the desire to forgive was Jane's desire to communicate to her husband that she had been severely hurt by his past betrayal of her. She had forgiven him mentally but not emotionally. Using Guided Imagery and Music, Jane expressed the anger she felt to him and forgave him for his past. Shortly after this, her colon condition and her marriage began to improve.

For many people it is just as difficult to express joy, enthusiasm and love as it is to express anger, hatred and other socially unacceptable emotions. We often suppress our loving feelings because we think that their expression will make us vulnerable, soft or weak. When you love someone, you are vulnerable to them; what they do or say has an impact upon you. When you love someone, you are also vulnerable to loss; there is always the possibility a friend or partner could die, move away or stop loving you.

Some people would rather not love than take the risk of suffering a loss of some kind. While this is common enough in people of all ages, it seems particularly common among the elderly. Many older people choose to die shortly after their life-long partner; it is unfortunate that they do not take the risk of continuing to love.

Many beliefs common in our society serve to suppress joy, love and enthusiasm. One of these is a confusion between egotism and self-love. This false belief says, "It is egotistical to do something you truly enjoy doing–work and play should be separated." Both men and women have real problems in expressing love or feelings because of cultural programming that devalues love. They often suppress their emotional selves, and in doing so, their love. These people often devalue any expression of love with these beliefs: "Love is weak." "If I love someone, I will only get hurt." "Love is beneath me." "Love is too confining; I do not want that kind of commitment."

The suppression of love is ultimately as harmful as the suppression of anger or hate because it leaves one in a lonely, alienated position. Since one refuses to give, one cannot receive love or joy from others. Eventually life becomes routine, boring and devoid of much feeling, worth or meaning. Anger and depression can creep in, along with feelings of hopelessness, to undermine the immune system and make one vulnerable to disease.

We do not usually think about suppressed love as a source of illness, yet we are aware that depression often precedes many serious illnesses. Life changes such as the death of a spouse, divorce, or the loss of a child often are important stress factors that bring on the depression . Some are so hurt at such a loss that they refuse to love again, or to recognize the possibility that the loss of one relationship can lead to other relationships just as deep and loving. Others can live through such losses and overcome the grief and depression that follows, going on to love again.

Arthritis in the hands and feet is very likely related to a refusal to give and receive love freely. It represents a refusal to express your love for fear of being rejected or thought to be weak. Many older people come to a place in their lives where they are afraid of the thought of their own deaths, yet uncomfortable with old ways of living. They do not know where they belong, but are unable to take the risk of beginning new relationships that might end in loss.

They hold on to the past instead of giving freely of their love and joy in life. As a result, there are blockages in the joints of their hands and feet. These blockages are related to deep feelings of insecurity and a refusal to express love freely for fear of vulnerability.

Better to choose to take the risk of loving than to cripple your life at any age from fear of giving and receiving. The courage to express love rather than block or suppress it can do wonders for your overall health and the vitality with which you live life. Joy and enthusiasm are closely related to love; they are, in a sense, love in action–they express in action the love that one has for life. Joy is the expression of your preferences in life. Enthusiasm is the deep passion that you have for these preferences. The expression of love through the pursuit of your preferences brings good health.

Chapter Eight

Self-Image and Healing

The symbolic way an illness expresses itself in the body depends on the self-image of the ill person. Certain illnesses, particularly those that involve the skin and the mobility of the body, represent a rigid or negative self-image. Rheumatoid patients, for instance, tend to perceive their bodies as firm, enclosed, and well-delineated. They often interpret Rorschach ink blots as rigid forms: "a man in armor," "a cement-covered post," or "a sea crab with a hard shell." Rheumatoid patients seem to have a rigid physical image of life and themselves even before they get arthritis. The therapist of one arthritic patient described the patient's hands before she evidenced any arthritic problems as "not only immobile but lifeless and inert." The physical rigidity and stiffness of arthritis usually corresponds to a mental and emotional rigidity.

In the book *Body Image and Personality*, Arehart-Treichel (1980) wrote: "One could conceive of the arthritic as a person who has certain unacceptable impulses over which he is so fearful of losing control that he has found it necessary to convert his body into a containing vessel whose walls would prevent the outbreak of those impulses...selectively utilizing a particular layer of his body...to achieve a protective wall about him..."

A positive, flexible self-image is the best basis for good health. Self-image together with choice are the two most important factors in recovering from an illness. Self-image is the picture that we hold of ourselves both consciously and unconsciously. This image sets the boundaries of who we are and gives meaning to our identities. Self-image can be compared to the banks of a river that contain the fluidity of our identities. Self-image sets the limits on what we think, feel and do. Each of us has many separate identities; we act, feel and think in different ways according to circumstances. We all play many roles in our lifetimes.

The current of the river that gives the water of life direction is self-esteem and self-love. If this current is missing, there can be no growth or direction to your life; the result is stagnation. This stagnation can lead to depression, anger, imbalance, and eventually illness. If your self-image is a narrow one, you become like a stagnant river that gets slower and thinner until it dries up, leaving no room for life, laughter or tears. Your self-image may even become so narrow that your desire to live declines, and with it your health. Your self-image contains all the feelings and thoughts of your life within it and determines where your river will flow. During an illness, the banks of your river become narrower and more constricted so that only a trickle of life energy flows through you.

One of the first steps in healing your self-image is to honestly explore the self-image stored within your subconscious mind. One way to arrive at this image is to reach a light state of relaxation and begin to write out everything about your self-image without judging or editing it. The next step is to take what is written and to summarize it in one sentence, then in one word. An example of this may be a person who sees herself as alone in the world, without support or help. This viewpoint could be reduced to the words "outcast," "orphan," or "outsider." You may need to ask for help in arriving at your self-image. You can do this by talking to a friend, counselor or family member. The way you see yourself may be different than how others see you. Then decide if this image is healthy, or if you want to replace it.

Understanding the Hopeless, Helpless Self-Image

Many illnesses occur because individuals have taken on a self-image of despair and hopelessness that compromises their immune systems and creates a bodily climate where illness can flourish. Many people go through an initial stage of illness in which they feel as though they are either a hopeless martyr or helpless victim to their illness. The self-image of victim or martyr brings out the weakest part of the self when you need strength and courage the most. These negative self-images are blockages to your healing. Despair, anxiety and hopelessness are emotional choices that affect the chemistry of our bodies, weakening them.

Both victims and martyrs refuse to take responsibility for their part in creating an illness. With this refusal, unfortunately, they also give up their healing power. It is always someone else or something else that is responsible for their illness and suffering. And the one who should be punished is a doctor, parent, spouse, child or even the Creator. Through their suffering, victims and martyrs hope to get special favors and attention from others or from God.

Illness often brings out the part of you that is a victim or martyr–the weakest part of you. It brings out your underlying fears, unfinished business and the emotional pains that play a major role in the creation of an illness. To transform a helpless, hopeless image of yourself, it is necessary to express your feelings about your illness and to explore your beliefs concerning it. If you believe you have no control over an illness, you relinquish your power over it. The best attitude toward an illness is a determination to fight and overcome it.

Numerous research studies have found personality patterns that underlie many illnesses including heart disease, cancer, and asthma among others. These personality patterns often include a negative self-image and a deep sense of personal worthlessness. This negative self-image may be disguised by other images that seek approval from others. Negative self-images are often related to traumatic childhood events and lead to problems of insecurity, helplessness and hopelessness in times of stress.

155

Creating a Positive Self-Image

To recover from an illness, it is necessary create and focus on a positive image of yourself, one that is broad enough to contain your deepest aspirations. You then begin to desire, expect and imagine yourself stepping into that image. You allow the banks of your identity stream to expand outward to include more of the life energy that can flow through you. When you become aware of your participation in creating an illness, do not punish yourself or feel guilty. Be grateful for this knowledge and use it to create a new image of yourself, without whatever destructive pattern it represented.

Your self-image always sets the limits of your reality. If you find it impossible to *imagine* a healthier, happier self, *creating* it will be impossible. You can assist in your own healing by seeing yourself as perfect at this time in your life, and by loving yourself totally and completely. This kind of unconditional self-love means accepting all parts of yourself, including negative aspects such as anger, depression or resentment. Acceptance of yourself is necessary to forgive whatever mistakes you may have made.

Self-image problems are most often indicated by skin irritations and ailments. When I began working with Brian, his self-image was low and he had trouble seeing himself as a successful person, since he had been unemployed for many years despite his intelligence and education. Brian's self-image was graphically symbolized by a chronic skin irritation on his penis. Brian said that this irritation appeared in bands that wept as though he were being whipped. The meaning of this skin irritation, he felt, was a self-image that felt whipped and emasculated in relationship to his male sexuality and power.

Meanwhile, Brian used women sexually and financially. He continued to have one unsuccessful relationship after another. Whenever he had intercourse, this skin irritation would reappear in response to his guilt over his sexuality. Brian's ideal self-image was as a spiritual-aesthetic man. He punished and abandoned women the way he felt his grandmother and mother had abandoned

156

him. His self-image as a spiritual man was inconsistent with the way he exploited women sexually, financially and emotionally. Brian said that this skin irritation disappeared after he stopped emasculating himself with guilt over his sexuality and began acting responsibly with women.

The Ideal Image Needed for Healing

Lawrence LeShan is a researcher who examined the healing methods of successful healers to discover the processes they had in common. He found they all focused on the unity of all things, and a person's power as part of this unity. LeShan found that successful methods of holistic healing are based on visualizing the perfect body pattern that can then be compared to the present ill form. This ideal form is like the pattern with which a master shoemaker creates his shoes. The healing process that LeShan discovered is one that focuses not on the physical reality of an illness, but on its healing.

To reach this state of healing, LeShan initially used images and symbols. He visualized the sick person and healer as two trees on opposite sides of a hill with the tops visible to each other. From one viewpoint they looked like two separate trees, but inside the hill, the two root systems met and were one. These two trees though unique were really one. Since their roots affected the soil and the atmosphere, so the universe was affected.

While the symbolism for healing through oneness can be different in each case, LeShan chose to reach a state he called "clairvoyant reality," in which the healer and ill person are united. LeShan discovered that this mystical clairvoyant reality is the same reality as that of the modern quantum physics. In his book, *The Medium, the Mystic and the Physicist*, LeShan shows how the statements of modern physicists are consistent with those made by healers and mystics. In this quantum mystical reality, individual events and objects exist, but their individuality is secondary to their

157

being part of a pattern of a larger unity. This unity makes it possible for miracles of healing to occur.

The steps in transcendent healing and mystical healing depend upon an awareness that all things are really one thing, which is spirit. Healing depends upon recognizing the spiritual self and a willingness to change mentally, physically, and spiritually.

Mystical healing depends upon recognizing that the real nature of the ill person is a perfect one, free of illness. That real nature can be realized if the ill person has faith in his or her own inner spirit and is willing to desire, expect and imagine whatever changes are needed to be whole. (Holmes, 1938)

There have been numerous well-documented physical healings. If not followed up with changes in the consciousness they symbolize, these conflicts often reappear in some similar illness. David's situation was one of the saddest examples of this phenomenon. He was miraculously healed of an inoperable stomach cancer with the help of a healing group of which I was an occasional member. This group was organized around the minister, John, of the church I then attended.

John had taken a church sabbatical to go to California to study under Lawrence LeShan. The group practiced LeShan's methods of mystical healing through a form of laying-on of hands. After several healing sessions with this group, David was elated to find that X-rays showed his cancerous stomach tumor had miraculously disappeared. Meanwhile, David continued to feel depressed and anxious about his life. There were obviously some issues he "could not stomach" that he needed to face, but was unable to resolve. Before long the cancer returned, and David died soon after.

Ideal healing of whatever kind needs to encompass not just the physical illness, but the conflict that produced it. I create individualized visualization tapes for critically ill people that focus not just upon the removal of the cancerous tumor or other symptom, but upon the conflict that the person recognizes it represents.

Achieving the Right Body Image for You

The right body for each of us is unique to ourselves. Cultural images of what is desirable or admired often open us to unhealthy identifications with someone else's idea of what we should be. This societal image prevents us from accepting and loving ourselves as we are. What is your ideal healthy body? It may have nothing to do with cultural images of health. Trying to live up to cultural ideas of a perfect body can be an ego trap that prevents you from accepting and realizing your uniqueness. Many of those people who look slim and youthful according to cultural standards may neglect emotional and mental and spiritual needs that later manifest as illness.

It is a common misconception that athletes are optimally healthy. Their competitive postures may actually be destructive to their health. When obsessive competitiveness is motivated by fear or low self-esteem, the chronic exercise of the athlete can be viewed as a type of stress. Several studies indicate that athletes die significantly more often from cancer than non-athletes. One survey of 8,000 college athletes suggests that cancer of the prostate and the digestive tract are more common among these athletes than in the general population (Pelletier, 1979). Cancer in the stomach or prostate indicates feelings are being controlled or suppressed. Athletic competitiveness may often discourage these feelings from being released or expressed in health ways.

Athletes sometimes focus on body training with little attention paid to their mental and emotional states. A few destructive results of an overly competitive attitude are numerous injuries, a greater need for surgery, and a much higher number of disabilities among the young. The great emphasis on competitiveness often devalues the quality of the experience for the athlete. As Pelletier states, "Optimum health is a qualitative, not a quantitative aspect of physical exercise." (Pellitier, 1979).

159

Self-Image as the Central Energy
Behind Carol's Psoriasis

Carol suffered from chronic psoriasis, an inflammatory skin disease characterized by flaking off and itching of the skin all over her body. Carol had an important position that involved interaction with the public. She felt insecure and threatened by the competition of subordinates whom she felt were as talented as she. Using relaxation, music and imagery, Carol focused on her illness and asked for an image of it. The image that appeared to her was of a statue disintegrating.

This image of her illness suggested to her that she was concentrating too much on appearances and status, to bolster her self-esteem. Carol also felt frustrated and irritated from not expressing her unique dreams and abilities. The constant threat and irritation this attitude brought with it was symbolized by her skin disease. Just like the statue, Carol felt she was in a prestigious place, but immobile and disintegrating. It was necessary to replace this self-image with a new one. The healing image she received was that of a seeker. The new healing image she received was that of a parachutist, in a jumpsuit, who came crashing through a plate glass window. For Carol, this image represented her as a seeker who dived into life without fear, to pursue and live up to her dreams and principles. Through meditation, Carol stepped into the image of the parachutist and felt the courage that was available to her within that image. This image allowed her to focus her courage and realize her dreams.

Healing Destructive Self-Images of Childhood

The source of illness is often the self-image we carry with us from childhood. In many illnesses, early childhood events and the resulting self-images predispose a person to disease. There is much evidence that the loss of a parent in childhood or an anguished childhood may be related to the development of cancer.

Dr. Carol Thomas of Johns Hopkins Medical Institution, in Baltimore, collected extensive data on 1,337 young, healthy medical students. Today many of them have reached middle age, and they include some fifty who now have cancer. Thomas found that those who contracted cancer reported a lack of closeness to parents during their childhood. 30% indicated that their fathers were not steady, warm or companionable; only 9.5% of healthy subjects felt this way.

During the 1960s, Dr. LeShan suspected that the length of time a person remained the youngest child might influence his later susceptibility to cancer. LeShan studied 200 families that had at least one cancer patient among their offspring. Results of this research showed that persons with cancer tended to have had a shorter period of being the youngest child than their cancer-free siblings, especially when another sibling arrived before they were two years old. This suggests that feeling deprived of parental attention and affection, particularly attention from your father,* can increase your vulnerability to cancer. Only children are less likely to get cancer than those with siblings. Thomas's study seems to indicate that the more attention you received as a child, especially as an infant, the more likely you are to be protected from cancer, and almost none of those who contracted cancer had been only children.

To put this in perspective, though, while only 0.2% of only children contracted cancer as adults, they also accounted for 50% of those with heart attacks and 39% of the mentally ill in the test group. Excessive parental inputs or parental dominance may predispose one to heart attacks or mental illness.

Thomas found that even before individuals come down with cancer, they tend to interpret Rorschach's projective tests rather morbidly. While healthy subjects tend to see positive images, prospective cancer patients tended to see pathological images like tumors, death, parasites and bacteria. A typically ominous response from a student who later developed cancer was, "a dead

---

*Mother's love is typically given unconditionally; father's love typically needs to be earned.

man seen from the feet." One of those students who later contracted cancer was a Dr. Peter E., the son of a prominent medical man. He was brought up in cultivated surroundings and had attended an Ivy League university. His parents had not shown him much affection as a child. Shortly before his fortieth birthday he had a seizure and was found to have inoperable cancer. He died six months later. (Arehart-Treichel, 1980)

In contrast to the lack of attention and affection that cancer patients receive, rheumatoid arthritis patients are often first born, last born, or only children who have an excessively dominating, strict parent; the other parent typically being weak, ineffective and completely overshadowed. As first born, last born or only children, more was generally expected of them. Most rheumatoid arthritis patients are also women who have difficulty accepting their sexual role. (Arehart-Treichel, 1980)

Releasing negative feelings about traumatic events in childhood can speed recovery from illness. Recovering from an illness is changing those parts of yourself, developed in childhood, that were wounded or deprived in some way. One of those parts of yourself is the "hurt child" within who clamors for attention and love, and it can take over your life unless its needs are satisfied. The "hurt child" within is not a nostalgic abstraction or technique; it is a real living part of your personality that may have to be healed to prevent or cure major illness. If there is a "hurt child" within that has not been satisfied, in times of crisis this child may take over and prevent you from living your life in an adult, responsible and fulfilled way.

There are a number of effective ways to release the injuries of your "hurt child," either alone in mediation or with the help of a therapist. One of these is to, in your imagination or in a relaxed meditative state, go back to and relive those childhood painful experiences, in order to resolve them. You do this by protecting and changing the reaction of the child. You become the child and act, feel, resolve and forgive what you could not then.

Jean, whom I once counseled, had a severe gastrointestinal problem and heart disease. Using Guided Imagery and Music she returned, in meditation, to her childhood home and cut her dominating and hostile father in little pieces and smeared them all around the room. When this was completed, she cleared her body with a golden light and used this light to put her father's body back together again and to heal her mother. She said this was the first time she had ever felt a sense of true forgiveness toward her father, whose dominating ways had traumatized her childhood.

It should be remembered that exercises of this kind are done to clear the subconscious mind; there is no intention to do actual physical harm. Anger in imagery is not the same as true aggression; it can and does heal. Feelings of guilt for expressing anger left from your childhood come when you assume you have no right to express that anger. It is important to honestly face your anger, express it appropriately, and then forgive yourself and the others involved.

When angry feelings concerning your childhood have been replaced with peace, healing has occurred. Forgiveness is not just a spiritual thing; it has a profound effect on your physical body. There is no way to fake or intellectualize forgiveness, because there is an unmistakable physical and emotional change that accompanies it.

For what reasons would rheumatoid arthritis or cancer patients have learned to withhold anger as a child? They may not have been allowed to express anger, particularly if they had domineering parents who withheld love as a form of punishment when they did. Perhaps some arthritic patients are afraid to express rage, anger and resentment because they have learned the people around them will deprive them of the emotional support they need. Arthritics may be so afraid of losing love or support that they sacrifice their own integrity and life to appease those around them. To survive their childhood, arthritics may have contracted with a parent to always please others and to never express anger. (Ariehart-Treichel, 1980)

An attitude of repression or suppression can be healed in a number of creative ways. You can create a set of ideal parents who will allow your child within to express him- or herself freely and be the loving parents your inner child never had. Another way is for you to become the nurturing parent who gives that child all it needs. This can be done by meeting your inner child, in meditation on a regular basis, either with or without the help of a psychotherapist. In meditation, you can go to a special place and meet your "hurt child" and allow that child to let you know what it needs. Its needs may surprise you! If you fulfill these needs in meditation or in the normal living of life, this child is healed, and that heals you. If the child within you feels loved and approved you become more peaceful and healthy.

If there are incidents in childhood in which you were shamed and abused in some way, you can change your reaction to what occurred. You can use the strengths and abilities you now have to defend yourself. You do not change what the other person did or said, but you do change your emotional reaction to it. By *choosing* your reaction, instead of it being something that just happens, you reclaim your power over the situation.

If you have a Type A personality and want to establish new healthier patterns, you can regain the childlike playfulness of your past by getting in touch with the free child within you that was lost somewhere in your childhood. Observe a time in your childhood in which you were playful, creative and childlike. First go as a reporter, observing what this child was doing. Then step into the body of the child–feel and experience what it was like to be joyous, free, spontaneous and creative. Allow yourself to play when you need to in your daily life. Carl Jung, in a time of healing crisis, spent much time constructing things out of blocks. This childlike activity helped him regain his lost freedom and creativity.

The child within will continue to interfere with your adult world if it does not get the kind of love it needs. If you were always criticized and belittled as a child, it will need approval and encouragement. If you were ignored as a child, it will need your attention. Releasing your inner child will free you from its interference and allow you to meet your adult needs of health and happiness. Satisfying its needs at a time convenient to you will prevent it feeling the need to clamor for attention when you are trying to handle an adult situation.

164

Chapter Nine

Messages of Two Main Killers–
Heart Attack and Cancer

The two major causes of death and disability in the United States are heart attack and cancer. Since these illnesses often occur in middle age, there are indications that they are created by our conflicts and life-styles and thus can be prevented. Resolving the internal conflicts symbolized by these illnesses is even more important to our health than are food and exercise.

The Message of Heart Attack

To understand the message of a heart attack, we need to look at the physical and mental life before the attack occurred. The energy that is related to the heart is tied to issues of love, particularly self-love and love for intimate others. The common way of dealing with a heart attack is to try to negate its destruction through purely physical means such as changing diet and exercising more. *Although these means are helpful, they do not reach the core, or "heart," of the matter; they do not listen to the underlying message of the disease.* To view a heart attack as a symbol or metaphor, it is necessary to look at what we associate with the heart. We most often associate its function with feelings, especially love; whether satisfied, frustrated or rejected love. When there is a problem with your feelings, particularly with difficulty in expressing love for yourself and others, then there is likely to be a problem with the heart and circulatory system. The central issue around a heart attack or heart problem is, "How did I harden or make a blockage against expression of my loving feelings?"

Most cases of heart disease start with a clogging or constriction of the veins and muscles either in the heart or circulatory system. Hypertension is a symptom that often precedes a heart attack. The research of Graham and his associates has identified the most common mental attitude associated with hypertension as feeling threatened with harm and having to be ready for anything. Hypertensive people feel in danger–that anything could happen at any time from any side. Therefore, they feel they have to be prepared to meet all possible threats and to be on guard. (Graham, Lundy, Benjamin, Kabler, Lewis, Kunish and Graham, 1958) It is noteworthy that hypertension is most common in African-Americans and in older people, who often feel oppressed and threatened by the larger society.

The way in which a hardening of the heart is expressed on a physical level has been discussed by Harold Wolff. His research identified what happens to the body when an individual's mental-emotional attitude is one that "hardens" his heart to himself and others; there is an increase in the constriction of heart and blood vessels, as if in anticipation of blood loss. The hypertensive patient might be viewed as overcompensating for consciously or subconsciously anticipated injury. (Wolf, S. & Goodell, 2nd edition, *Harold G. Wolff's Stress and Disease*, 1968)

Those who have studied hypertensive patients have often found them poised for aggression, but restraining aggressive activity to avoid conflict. Their particular way of dealing with stress is through restrained aggression. Those individuals with hypertension who were interviewed by Graham and his associates felt that they constantly had to be prepared to meet all possible threats. Typical statements made by hypertensive patients were these: "I had to be ready for anything," or "It was up to me to take care of all the worries," or "Nobody is going to beat me. I'm ready for anything." or "I've been sitting on the lid all my life, waiting for the explosion." (Graham, Lundy, etc., 1958) A heart attack is an explosion of the heart. It is unfortunate when the emotional pressure that refuses to love self and others is not identified and healed before this explosion occurs.

It is likely that the inner barrier to feeling love, especially self-love, begins somewhere in childhood when both physical and emotional destruction began. On a purely physical level, this destruction was a constriction or buildup of cholesterol in the veins and arteries of the body. It has been proven that this buildup begins very early, even in children and young adults. Somewhere in childhood, perhaps even as young as ten years of age, some important decisions were made that formed a pattern that cut out joy and feelings, especially those of self-love. This defensive posture placed a barrier to valuing, recognizing and expressing loving feelings toward oneself and others. The child decided it was too painful to feel, to play or to express himself freely. He then chose to invest himself in activities that were less emotionally fulfilling. From this perspective, the child began to lose a sense of his self-esteem and began closing down the center of his joyful, loving feelings– the heart center.

Type A Personalities and Heart Disease

The most comprehensive work on personality and cardiovascular disorders is that of Friedman, Rosenman and their colleagues in the categorization of Type A and Type B personalities. One of the early clues that a consistent pattern of behavior might exist among coronary patients came from the upholsterer who noticed that patients' chairs were worn only on the front edges, as if people had been sitting in tense expectation. Another clue came from a study of the difference in heart disease between husbands and wives of Junior Leaguers in San Francisco. The wives in this study suffered significantly less heart disease than their husbands, even though their eating habits were exactly alike. Female hormonal differences were not a likely factor since white women in other countries had as high an incidence of heart disease as men, and black women in the United States were slightly more susceptible to heart disease than black men. Most or all of the husbands in the study, though, had high-stress jobs, while most or all the wives did not work outside the home.

Over years of observation, Friedman and Rosenman developed a detailed profile of the heart disease-susceptible Type A personality and his less-stressed, healthier Type B counterpart. The Type A personality has two traits that set him or her apart from others. These are an excessively competitive drive and a chronic, continual sense of time urgency. Along with these two characteristics, Type A individuals also showed easily aroused hostility. Their lives are oriented around goals, deadlines and objectives which cause them to experience continual stress from "hurry sickness." Type A personalities are often successful people who live up to the American ideal but die early from coronary artery disease.

In contrast to the Type A personality, the Type B personality is free of the frantic sense of time urgency so typical of Type As. This pressure is never a factor in their leisure time, since Type B personalities *take* their leisure time–without guilt. If they are ambitious, their goals are based upon personal values. They do not feel the need to measure themselves constantly against their peers or in terms of the number of their achievements.

Highly stressed, less healthy Type A personalities can learn much from emulating the example of the Type B low-stress mode of behavior. Type B personalities have a sense of self-esteem that comes from having and working toward life goals that transcend material and social success. Type B personalities base their self-esteem on inner rather than outer validation, and they accept their strengths or weaknesses. In contrast, Type A personalities are never sure of their self-esteem, so they are constantly seeking outside validation for reassurance.

Since the Type B personalities work from an inner sense of self-validation rather than from competition, they are not compulsively trying to compete with or to seek approval from others. Consequently, they are free of the hostility which so often accompanies a strong competitive drive. Type B individuals frequently allow themselves time for quiet contemplation in their own self-styled meditation. When confronted with a problem or a task, Type B personalities consider the alternatives and think through an effective course of action.

The typical Type B method of coping contributes to a more creative output of work and behavior than that of the typical Type A. In the Type A's eagerness to get things done as fast as possible, they may respond in stereotyped ways that are not appropriate. Ultimately, these old responses cause them to make errors in judgement, since no time is taken to consider new more creative approaches. Type A's do not use their creativity or intuition to solve problems, and have limited flexibility.

For a Type A personality to change his or her life, it is necessary to change the value system supporting it. The basic issue behind heart disease is a lack of self-love–a lack of a caring and compassionate intimacy with your uniqueness. Self-love is impossible if you are constantly looking for outside validation to reinforce your self-worth and self-esteem. Self-worth depends on the realization that each of us is a spiritual being–a piece or spark of God–and that we do not have to earn self-worth; it is given to each of us. Self-esteem, in contrast, is based on the earned awareness of our value as unique beings.

Cardiovascular Disease and An Attitude of Struggle

H. Wolff described the symbolic correspondence to coronary artery disease as an attitude of seeing life as a constant struggle. This constant struggle is described as the "Sisyphus" reaction.

Sisyphus is a figure in Greek mythology who was confined to Hades and was required to push a great rock up a steep hill. Whenever he was near the top, the rock rolled down again, requiring him to continually struggle without accomplishment or reward. Individuals with coronary artery disease are like Sisyphus, constantly struggling with little time for relaxation or enjoyment.

The person with increased serum cholesterol behaves biologically as if he or she were undertaking vigorous effort, and the body correspondingly does what it would do under such circumstances. (Wolf, S. and Goodell, 1968) Typical statements found in the Graham research study made by coronary artery patents were these: "There is just not enough time to do all I need to do." "I'm always in a hurry." "There is too much to do, and not enough time to do it." (Graham, Lundy, etc. 1958)

Alice and Hypertension

Underlying this attitude of struggle is one that sees an act as valuable only if it requires struggle or suffering. Unfortunately, this emphasis upon struggle is part of the cultural pattern of our predominately male-oriented world. As more and more women become involved in the world, these women are also subject to the male-dominated values that go with it, unless they change those values.

Alice is a successful business woman who came to me for a holistic assessment of her high blood pressure condition. Alice had a sense of desperation about her life and a premonition that if she did not do something to change her life-style, she would have a heart attack.

Although Alice was highly successful in her work, she was in a position in which she felt constantly under pressure to perform better than others around her. Her fear was that her superiors, several older men, would find out she was not as perfect or as successful as she appeared to be. Alice performed at an accelerated pace, not letting down for a moment.

Alice was the daughter of a competitive, unnurturing mother and a wealthy, neglectful father. Alice lived in an expensive, showy way. Neither Alice nor her husband took time to be intimate with each other or their daughter. Although Alice saw her pattern as a destructive, unhappy one, she was reluctant to make the changes necessary to create a different one, as her life seemed successful. Her ideal dream would have been to live a more relaxed, creative life with time to be more creative and expressive with her family.

The central energy behind Alice's hypertension was a compulsive drive to gain self-esteem by being better than others and by getting approval from certain important male figures. To change her life style, Alice would have to transcend the common view that values the driving, ambitious person as successful and apparently heroic. Alice would have to begin to live by internal values of integrity, responsibility and a self-love that allowed her to enjoy herself and to express her uniqueness.

The dramatic success of the San Francisco Recurrent Coronary Prevention project, created by Friedman and his associates, can be attributed to the constant demand that the participants be aware of their specific destructive Type A behaviors, and that they take daily steps to change these. This demand is made in repetitive individual and group counseling in which participants confront and deal with destructive patterns in themselves and others. (Friedman & Ulmer, 1984)

Similar programs designed to address the specific disease creating processes typical of an illness can be created for other illnesses such as arthritis and cancer. These programs would begin by using what we already know through research to be a central conflict in many with that disease. For instance, those who have arthritis tend to inhibit feelings, and those who have cancer often feel despair concerning finding meaning in life. This despair often originates in childhood loss of love.

The Message of Cancer

Look at the message cancer brings. Cancer is a bodily state in which primitive, egotistical, nonproductive cells are multiplying, overwhelming and replacing healthy productive ones. The living, growing self is being replaced by a stagnant body. Immunologists classify cancer as a "nonself." Cancer may symbolically represent the stagnant, ungrowing self that has replaced the vital, growing self one could be.

Cancer involves an identity crisis in which the patient not only fights for physical survival; but to reinstate his or her unique true self. (Wolf, S. & Goodell, 1968) Common in the background of cancer patients is a loss or event that stimulated despair or anxiety that blocked further growth. For those who have cancer, the important question to ask is, "How and why did I stop growing in my own unique way?"

In LeShan's research of the emotional factors preceding cancer, he found the two most important were the loss of a relationship that had given meaning to life, and an inability to express hostility. (LeShan, 1977) Carl and Stephanie Simonton identified four predisposing personality characteristics of cancer patients:

l) a great tendency to hold resentment and a marked inability to forgive;

2) a tendency toward self-pity;

3) a poor ability to develop and maintain meaningful, long-term relationships, and

4) a very poor self-image.

The Simontons noticed an interaction between a patient's belief system and the course of treatment. Patients who experienced spontaneous remission had often undergone a process of revising their beliefs and creating new self-images.

Repressed Emotions Beneath Cancer

Graham and his associates identified the typical attitude of those who have cancer as a deep dissatisfaction and despair of being the wrong sex, race or social class or having the wrong life circumstances. Typical statements of cancer patients are, "I wish I could start over again," "If I had been a man (woman), I could have been happy or successful," "I wish it was like it used to be," and "If I could do it all over again, I would do it differently." (Graham, Lundy, etc., 1958)

Cancer represents a suppressed anger that one feels hopeless to express. Since this anger is denied and unrecognized, it often is present in the form of anxiety and despair. LeShan's therapeutic work with 71 cancer patients found that 68 had a feeling of despair that predated the onset of their cancer, and that this despair was part of their general orientation to life. The source and circumstances of despair were different for men than women. Men tended to feel despair over their jobs; they strongly identified themselves with work and became depressed if they had lost their jobs or retired. The source of despair for women was often tied to a lack of fulfillment in their role as housewife or mother, especially after their children left, or when their marital relationship was less than satisfying.

Housewives get cancer 54% more often than the general population and 157% more often than women who work outside the home, according to research from the University of Oregon. (Siegel, Bernie, *Love, Medicine and Miracles* (tape), 1986) Carcinogens in the kitchen do not seem to be the problem, for domestic workers in other people's kitchens get far fewer cases of cancer. The central issue for housewives with cancer seems to be the despair that often accompanies their role.

Lydia Temoshok researched the effects of a Type C behavioral pattern, the core of which according to her is a repression of feelings, especially anger. Temoshok's research found that this kind of behavior put people at risk for cancer development because it weakens the immune system. Temoshok attributes the development of malignancy to a breakdown in the immune system, as a result of feeling stuck in a stressful situation where one feels unable to flee or fight.

To test her theory, Temoshok divided 56 patients with melanoma, a form of skin cancer, into the categories "expressive" and "nonexpressive." She found that the nonexpressive Type C behavioral pattern of emotions was correlated with faster growing, more virulent cases of cancer. The opposite was true of those who did not demonstrate this behavior. Temoshok recognized that Type C behavior could be changed by a program that encouraged emotional flexibility to help people contact their feelings, soften their defenses, and change their relationships.

Type C is based upon a pledge of conformity to socially acceptable behavior. Angers and anxieties are hidden so deeply that often the person is not aware of them. Such a person often is brought up with the belief that nothing but kind, good thoughts are acceptable. This kind of demand prevents him or her from being honest and authentic. The symbolic core of cancer is being a false, inauthentic self as a result of having little depth of feelings. People with Type C behavior can then easily become the puppets or instruments of others, instead of becoming their true selves. Since they will not feel their negative feelings, they are unable to feel their positive ones. In the depth of those feelings, they would have found their identity, creativity and destiny.

Symbolism in the Location of Cancer

The place a cancer occurs is not accidental; it strikes those areas of the body that symbolize the main conflicts of your life. The main conflict is the loss of Self that results when a false self which represses feelings such as anger makes it impossible to be real. Melodie, who died of a brain tumor, was unable to process and deal with the shame she felt for being unwanted as a child. Claire with colon cancer held onto old resentments and was anxious about her security. Breast cancer is not something that just happens at random. It is related to anger concerning issues of self-love and nurturing. The breast for women symbolizes love and nurturing. For some women, cancer develops in response to an inability to nurture, which results in guilt and self-hate. Others experience a loss of identity after their children leave home.

For Ruth, the central issues of her breast cancer were old resentments from childhood that had influenced her and made it difficult for her to bear and nurture her own children. While her mother worked, Ruth was required to care for her three younger brothers, whom she felt she had raised. Ruth felt cheated of her childhood. Since she never was nurtured herself, Ruth felt anger and self-hate for her ambivalence toward nursing and rearing children. Ruth had many miscarriages and only one child, who left home at a young age. Much of the emotional healing needed by Ruth involved going back to childhood to heal the child within her who still felt unloved and angry, because she never got the love and nurturing it needed.

Problems in sexual adjustment or in the giving and receiving of sexual pleasure have been found to be related to cancer of the cervix in women. In one study, the personality profiles of 100 women with cervical cancer were compared to a group of women with cancer in other sites. Researchers found that those women who had cervical cancer had an aversion to sexual intercourse. There was also a higher frequency of divorce, desertion, unfaithful husbands, separation, lack of orgasmic satisfaction, and greater incidence of extra-marital affairs in the patients with cervical cancer than in women with other forms of cancer.

A Theoretical Basis of Cancer Originating in Anger as Anxiety

Cancer is a rapid growth of cells, as are the tumors character-istic of it. One plausible explanation of this excessive growth, not yet scientifically demonstrated, is that cancer originates from a mental condition of repeated and extended anxiety which triggers the repeated and extended release of the growth hormone tryptophan, which stimulates excessive growth. Anxiety is unidentified and repressed anger, fear, shame or hurt. When you experience anxiety over a prolonged period of time, your body reacts by stimulating a destructive chemical chain reaction.

A plausible theoretical basis for the relationship between anger and cancer is based upon a chemical chain reaction in the body that begins with a prolonged state of anxiety. When you hold anger that you refuse to identify for years and years, your brain (particularly the hypothalamus) sends a signal to the pituitary and the thymus to release tryptophan, a peptide that exists both in the brain and elsewhere in the body. This hormone triggers a neurotransmitter called serotonin that makes you feel calm and that produces a mental clarity to help you deal with the anxiety. This chemical is wonderful in times of crisis, but in excess together with tryptophan, can cause severe damage to the body.

Tryptophan is a growth hormone that your thymus releases during adolescence because you need hormones to make your muscles grow and become strong during that time. Tryptophan helps coordinate your growth during adolescence. If you begin to release this hormone in excess as an adult, you run the risk of activating latencies in the body such as diabetes and other diseases encoded on your DNA. Serotonin in excess can attack muscles and nerves and is often associated with depression. Both tryptophan and serotonin become excessive during periods of prolonged anxiety. (Lazaris, *Escaping the Suffocating Web of Anxiety* (Tape))

Healing the anxiety begins with an honest process of feeling and thinking. This is done by letting the anger surface from the subconscious where it is hidden. The anger needs to be felt and released, along with the belief complex that holds it in place. Part of this belief complex may be ideas that discount and deny the value of the expression of anger. Often with the denial of anger comes the denial of other more positive feelings, which are necessary to realize the genuine unique Self.

176

Chapter Ten

Transcending An Illness

Perhaps the highest truth about illness is that it's not the only means of growth. We can grow more elegantly through joy and love; we can create our health more easily and happily than our illness. However, as long as we have an illness, it is a powerful teacher that points us in the way of wiser and higher choices.

When your body is ill, it is giving you one of two kinds of messages; those that say, "Please help me," or those that say, "Pay attention and change." Both kinds of messages ask you to reach beyond the level of your conflict to a higher peace.

To transcend an illness is to go to the highest truth concerning it. Transcending is rising above the conflict and imbalanced level of an illness to a higher level of peace and balance. Only when you go within to your quiet mind or higher consciousness do you know how to transcend the conflict level.

When you become aware that healing is your responsibility, then symptoms of illnesses are messages that you can answer. If you learn to trust your body, it becomes your intimate friend who honestly reflects back to you what is happening and what areas of your life need to be focused upon and healed. When you listen to your body, part of you is showing compassion for another part.

Transcending an illness can only be done by the one who is ill because that person is the only one who can make the changes necessary for healing. A year ago, a physician examined my throat and told me he could find no trace of a goiter that had been there. Two years earlier, an endocrinologist gave me the prognosis, "You have a mild case of hypothyroidism with a Hashimoto's goiter, and I would expect it to progress. Your thyroid is beginning to be replaced by scar tissue. Your TSH is elevated. You have an inherited genetic tendency; its exact cause is unknown." Fortunately, I did not accept this prognosis and looked for the real cause of my illness, which was in my fear of expressing myself.

The highest truth about me was that I needed to give myself full permission to express talent I possessed to be a writer/poet and holistic counselor. I faced my inhibitions about expressing myself and resolved them at a higher level than that of tradition or authority. Transcending for me meant to reach and become the courageous self I was who gave me full permission to express my truth. This part of me had an integrity and honesty that looked at all aspects of my illness to know what needed to be healed in me.

Obstacles to Transcending

The greatest obstacle to transcending an illness is resisting not only its message and meaning, but the feelings and emotions that lie beneath those messages. To the extent that you fear and devalue your emotions, you avoid healing the real source of your illness that often lies hidden within them. To determine how you resist the message, notice what your first reaction is when you become ill or show symptoms of imbalance. Do you deny? ("I'm not really ill.") Are you defensive? ("It is the Doctor's fault." "It was something I ate.") Do you discount it? ("It's not really life-threatening.") Do you distract yourself? ("I think I will take a trip before I try to heal this.") Merely removing yourself from the conflicting situation does not change the consciousness that either created or allowed this conflict. If you do these things, you are guaranteed to not transcend an illness.

What do you use to avoid responsibility for your illness or problems? Unfortunately, our society and traditional medicine encourage us to see illness as a meaningless physical event. Societal denial reinforces and fuels personal resistance to transforming illness.

Steps in Transcending an Illness

Transcending an illness involves owning the pattern of thoughts and feelings that underlie it. Illnesses are always related to emotions such as fear, anger and sorrow that are destructive when they are resisted and not expressed and thus are stored and expressed symbolically in the body. To transcend an illness means that you stop resisting the awareness of emotions such as anger, fear, grief and despair and their supporting belief structures. Fear is often associated with heart disease, anger with arthritis and grief with asthma.

The first step in transcending an illness is to face the pattern behind your destructive emotions and feelings. Look at the following destructive patterns and recognize which of these fuels your anger, fear, hurt, sadness, despair or grief. Recognize that one or more of these destructive patterns can threaten your emotional, physical, mental and spiritual health. To be complete, healing has to come on all levels. Some destructive patterns that fuel illnesses are:

1. *Fear of abandonment*–rejection such as when you lose friends or a job.
2. *Fear of betrayal*–when you fear being betrayed or humiliated by others.
3. *Martyrdom*–with its punishment in which you feel unappreciated, overworked, and you punish others or your Soul and Higher Self (not yourself).
4. *Demanding Perfection*–always blaming and looking to others for answers rather than to your own creativity and peace.

5. *Defectiveness*–feeling shame, pain, sorrow.

6. *Entitled*–do not have to change because of your suffering. You are especially good or bad because of all your suffering and struggle.

7. *Dependency*–You cannot change until they do. You are totally dependent, devastated and threatened, and are always talking about impending devastation. (Victims assume this pattern.)

8. *Alienation*–self-sabotage, exclusion. No one will include you, you are separate.

These patterns create your future and feed your destructive root emotion. Identify which one of these patterns is yours and then one or two beliefs that are associated with it. See these beliefs and then change them. Suppose you have been unable to find employment in the work you wanted to do–logging, for instance. You feel abandoned and may have feelings of anger, fear, or despair. If these feelings are not expressed appropriately, you may become ill. The destructive beliefs that support these feelings may be: "I am discarded because I am not good enough," or, "The company betrayed me despite my loyalty and hard work," or, "I will never get another job again." You can change these beliefs by acknowledging that you *are* good enough. This situation can be seen as a challenge to bring out those talents within you that have lain dormant. Beliefs cannot be changed by removal, only by replacement. You cannot just stop believing something; you have to create a new, different, more healthy belief in its place.

The key to transforming this destructive pattern is to first own that it is yours and that in time it can produce disease. Your fear may precipitate a heart condition; your anger, arthritis; and your despair, cancer. Then replace the beliefs that support this pattern. Recognize what the source feeling is–betrayal, alienation, etc.–and then you can more easily identify the beliefs which support that emotion.

One way to transform an illness is by focusing on the central energy conflict (feelings of betrayal, abandonment, etc.) behind it, and feeling and knowing the impact that conflict is having upon the various areas of your life, such as health, work, relationships and spirituality. Say this out loud, and experience the feelings of that impact. Recognize the consequences of resisting your awareness, and of continuing the destructive pattern. What are the consequences to your health and to your life if you do not change? What will your angry, fearful, grieving or despairing thoughts and feelings do to your health?

Joan recognized the central conflict behind her stomach and liver cancer was perfectionism. Her cynical self-criticism (from feeling not perfect enough) caused her to look outside herself for rational reasons to blame others. It also produced a need to control her feelings and life through chronic worry and anxiety. To transform her illness, she encountered the shadow part of herself, which told her she needed to let go of her need to worry and control everything and everyone around her.

Shadow work in meditation can be very effective in transcending destructive patterns of emotions and the beliefs which support them. Relax and in meditation take your Higher Self with you to see that part of your shadow self that is your objector-protector. See yourself going down a long corridor to a room in which there is a shadowy figure whose face is dark. You are there to make peace with your shadow and to talk to it concerning the lies or conflicts in your life.

You can begin your dialogue with your shadow by asking, "What do you need from me to make peace?" or, "What lie am I living?" The shadow is not your negative ego; it is that part of you that objects to any kind of change, and seeks to protect you from things you are not ready to face. Be sure to have your Higher Self interpret the answer. For instance, if it asks for your heart, do not give it until your Higher Self interprets this. Is it asking for your love or for your heart, literally. In her dialogue with her shadow self, Joan asked, "What do I need from you to make peace?" The answer was her forgiveness. The shadow also keeps for you all the beautiful and powerful talents that you are not yet ready to accept. When you have identified in words your destructive pattern or patterns, such as "dependence on untrustworthy people" or "abandonment," then transform those words into images; see the images of your fear, anger, humiliation or such. Then turn those images into sounds–groans snarls, screams, screeches, etc.–and then into the silence beyond this, the silence of pure despair. Focus on that feeling, and feel yourself pushing it out of your body, out through your organs, bones, heart and lungs. Push out this fear, this despair, from wherever it is hidden, out through your skin, and transform it into a juice that oozes from you. Collect this juice and offer it to your Higher Self, or to God, to heal you and transform you. (Lazaris, *Transforming Personal Fear Into Amazing Success*, (tape,) 1994)

One way to transform an illness is to see what this conflict does to your abilities, talents and purposes, particularly your ability to love. When you encounter the shadow side of yourself, ask, "What have you stolen from me?" This part of yourself prevents you from realizing your health and your unique abilities. For instance, if you have chronic fatigue syndrome, your energy has been stolen from you.

Another way to transform an illness is through elegance. You focus on and pay attention to what you wish to become. This is the part of yourself that loves you totally, is not perfect, but is at peace. This is the ideal self you began envisioning in your Wellness circle. Through meditation, encounter this ideal self and explore your divinity–that part of yourself which is eternal, strong, loving and self-realizing. When you encounter this part of yourself, ask, "What is the beautiful, right thing about me that I have refused to recognize and appreciate?" This part of yourself is the gift of power beneath your illness you need to recognize and receive.

In focusing upon your well self, you envision what the essence of this new well person would be. You transcend an illness through feeling and recognizing the impact of the conflict behind your illness. By paying attention to your highest self, you then choose what you will do. Hopefully, you will decide to step into or merge with this new well self. Then you can let the universe handle the details of your healing by allowing yourself to receive whatever help comes to you physically, emotionally, mentally and spiritually. Much of healing is just allowing yourself to receive the love and power always there for you if you would only accept it.

Transcending the Fear in Hypertension and Other Diseases

Fear is a thought and a feeling of separation, of being alone, that threatens you and puts you in jeopardy. Fear is an instinctive response to danger. It is a great teacher and motivator, and accompanies both success and failure. Since fear is such a common emotion in our world, it seems to be automatic and therefore beyond our control, when actually we can understand and transcend it. Fear affects our emotional, physical, mental and spiritual selves and needs to be healed on all these levels if we are to be healthy.

Supposed or imagined fear manifests the same reactions in the physical body as actual danger; your thyroid shuts off, your thymus collapses, and your glands pump out the emergency chemicals cortisol, tryptophan and endorphines to help you cope with the danger. Fear is the root emotion and source of heart disease and hypertension.

The body of a person with hypertension is on constant red alert, ready for any and all danger, ready for fight or flight. Behind this condition is fear which needs to be owned, released and transcended. You can exercise and eat better, but until you face the fear you have not healed the primary source of heart disease. Our usual ways of handling fear–denial, distraction, avoidance, discounting and defensiveness–only guarantee that real and complete healing will not take place.

Feeling or having fear is not necessarily a problem; what you do with it can be hazardous to your health. There are definite steps to handle the fear behind hypertension (or the grief behind asthma, or the anger behind arthritis, or the despair behind cancer, etc.). Traditional western medical practice resists treating, or acknowledging the importance of these emotions in the healing of an illness, relying on allopathic methods to reverse or block the symptoms instead. Current mainstream medical practice has evolved from left-brain, logical, analytical, thinking, which denies, devalues and discounts the importance of imagination and emotions (feminine, right-brained, holistic). The emotions are the cause of, and the key to the healing of, disease. Your investment in a left-brained, logical mind-set may determine whether you can take the first step in healing the fear behind an illness.

The first step is to face your emotion (fear, grief, etc.) and accept it without lying to yourself, without resisting it by discounting, denying, etc. The second step is to recognize what specifically is being threatened or put into jeopardy by that emotion. Some things which fear threatens are:

(1) loss of your needs–survival, belonging, esteem, creativity/productivity, intuition, knowing and spirituality

(2) loss of power

(3) loss of your real self

(4) loss of success with all its attributes and awards

(5) loss of intimacy and caring–a withdrawal of affection and love

(6) threats of judgement and punishment from yourself or others

(7) pain and destruction

The third step in processing the fear behind hypertension is to consider the consequences of not dealing with the old root emotion. What is the jeopardy of going into denial, distraction or discounting of the seriousness of its threat? What are the consequences of the old action or inaction?

The fourth step is the commitment to learn from it. What is it that you can learn to change the old negative pattern? Suppose you have a fear that you will never be happy until you cause other significant people in your life to change. You are always dependent upon one destructive person after another. To overcome this pattern you learn to see that your happiness and independence is within your own power, and not based on what others do or don't do. Your commitment to learn from the fear has given you relief from it.

If you again become fearful, after earlier identifying its source, you can always give yourself a set period of time to be self-punishing, self-pitying and fearful. Do this with the conscious knowing that after a specific limited time, maybe 20 or 30 minutes, you will drop it. One helpful technique is to use a fear letter. Address this letter to yourself, telling yourself what really frightens you. Bring it out each day for three days to read again and to add to it. Then destroy it in three ways, such as tearing it up, burning it, and burying its ashes. This brings your emotions out of your subconscious and allows you to have the chance to see them in a different perspective. You may actually find that you have grown bored with them. Then you have overcome them.

The fifth step in transforming the destructive pattern behind an illness is focusing on the future self you desire to become. This is the self represented by your Wellness circle and its ideals. Discover what the feeling or resonance of that successful self is. How would you act, feel and respond to others if you were living from that resonance of success? What is it going to feel like when your fear, anger, hurt, despair, grief or other destructive pattern is gone?

The sixth and final step is a resolve to act and to have the resonance of wellness. Give out or radiate the quality of success you want to feel that replaces your old action. If the old pattern was fear, learn to trust yourself and others who demonstrate they are worthy of your trust. See what you want on the other side of fear, anger and despair and let that radiate out of you. This might be the side of yourself that was the gift hidden for you beneath your fear, anger and illness. (Lazaris, Ibid.)

Claiming the Gift of Power Beneath an Illness

People who have health problems related to fear often have special gifts that they could claim if they learn the lessons of how to use those gifts better. These people often have a phenomenal imagination and a vivid capacity to visualize. They can vividly imagine what will happen to them at the doctor's office when the needle goes in or the doctor listens to their hearts. It is little wonder their hearts respond with what is called the "white coat" phenomenon of doctor fear. Their capacity for great fear may grow out of other talents such as knowing who and how to trust. After years of experience around the issue of trust, they know when and to whom to give their trust, and trust only those who have earned it.

Many fearful people value the opposite of fear–intimacy–because they have experienced how fear destroys it, and therefore have a great capacity to be intimate. Many fearful people also are very intuitive because their psychic abilities give them an innate sense of knowing that warns them of danger and of what is right or wrong for them. Intuition is a correct knowing that just is, without any rational explanation. Fearful people often have a strong will and determination to survive. Since they have mastered the art of self-preservation, they have insights to help others and themselves not only to survive but to do things in new and visionary ways. (Lazaris, Ibid.)

Many gifts can come from illness. The issue of heart disease is often feeling controlled by fear, anger and frustration. Thus, the gift of power beneath heart disease is learning to give yourself self-esteem through living up to your principles of honesty, integrity and trust. The gift of power beneath cancer is no less than being a unique individual. This power comes when the mask or persona is dropped to allow the unique individual to emerge. This you is real because you respect and express your feelings and desires appropriately and honestly. Hidden within your specific healing ideal is a unique gift of power, important to your growth.

Transcending an illness is reaching and stretching to become part of the higher consciousness–the quiet mind within us. This higher consciousness can be compared to the blue sky above the clouds, that you reach in rising in an airplane above the earth. It is the peak of consciousness above the trees where you can at last see where you have traveled and why. From that peak, you can understand how a particular illness caused you to awaken in some

186

way. Without it, you may not have reached this peak of peace or knowledge where you now stand.

Hans Castorp, the hero in Thomas Mann's book, *Magic Mountain*, takes a journey up to a sanatorium in the Alps to heal and discover himself. After Hans has been at the sanatorium for many years he is no longer a naive young man. He puts on his skis and sets forth alone into the mountains. In the vast alpine silence of a snowstorm, he realizes he is lost. A little frightened, he drinks some port for strength. This port puts him to sleep as he leans against a snowbound mountain hut. There he has a beautiful dream of a landscape he has never seen before. In this lovely sunlight world, people gracefully move among stately columns, a scene of nobility and beauty. Into the scene come two witches who are silently tearing a child apart over a cauldron.

When he awakens, Hans recognizes the meaning of his vision. This is the knowledge of "Homo die" that in his creative divinity each person is the lord of both life and death. He discovered that more noble than physical life is the purity of his heart. More noble than death is the freedom of his power of thought and choice. Love, not reason, he realizes, is stronger than death, and it is the gentle force through which both form and civilization are created. Hans Castorp resolved, "For the sake of gentleness and love, man shall let death have no sway over his thoughts and with this I wake." That discovery allows him to go from superficial health, through illness, to a higher health.

Castorp, through a dream, found the real man dwelling within him. In that dream reality, he becomes whole; and this wholeness in him becomes part of nature, without separation. It is in silence, in the quietness of solitude or meditation, we too can transcend illness and come to the quiet place of our higher consciousness. This place sees life and death as part of one process, rather than as a conflict. It is a place that denies neither death or illness, but sees them as illusions in relationship to life and health.

The higher consciousness is eternal, timeless, and limitless. It knows we create our illness and so can create health instead. To reach this quiet place of higher consciousness, recognize you are spirit, *and your body is, too.*   Your openness to the spirit is spontaneously conveyed to your body; there is no separation and both are intimately linked.

The quiet mind sees everything clearly. It sees the conflicts within and without, but chooses neither to flee nor fight them. The witches of death and illness do not oppress a quiet mind that does not fear them.   The highest truth holds opinions rather than judgements of right or wrong. It seeks a common ground to resolve conflict. To find a common ground a change has to occur within people. The Berlin Wall did not come down because of the actions of leaders. It came down because individual people changed and no longer allowed it to contain them. When the people of Eastern Germany began fleeing their country in great numbers the wall could no longer contain them.

The Alchemy of Healing

To overcome the obstacles to healing, it is necessary to take the attitude of an adventurer, not only of the positive aspects but the dark, hidden side of yourself, your shadow side that created or allowed this illness. It is a mistake to attempt to transcend an illness by having only positive thoughts and feelings. To transcend an illness, you need to respect all of your emotions and recognize that if they are not expressed and released they can be internalized and then cause illness.

Thinking and feeling are interrelated. If you do not let yourself feel, you will not think well; and if you will not think, you can not feel deeply. Emotions such as anger and fear are not inherently good or bad. When negative emotions are expressed openly and honestly, they become positive tools to produce and motivate change.

You have to honestly ask what have been the benefits to the side of yourself that allowed or created this illness. What benefits

188

and manipulations do you get because of it? What is the resistance or fear that you have of its absence? When you become aware of the benefits you have the way it is, you can then *step back* from it and observe it from above and below you, to help you become objective.

Joan, a young woman with stomach cancer, recognized that she had suppressed and controlled her feelings of fear that she would not be perfect as a teacher or mother. To heal herself, she had to step back by feeling more and exploring her feelings. To encourage feeling more, she wrote spontaneously off the top of her head as much as she could. I encouraged her to read out loud what she had written, always asking herself, "What is the feeling behind what is happening to me?" She could explore the depth of her feeling by continuing to ask, "What is under that feeling?" until she came to her baseline feeling, which was self-pity.

You encounter your dark side (shadow self) to make peace and to transform it into something better. The false detachment of not allowing feelings can be replaced by a respect for your feeling, despair can be transformed to determination, confusion to vision, and stubbornness to openness. You can ask your dark side, "What strengths can you give me, if I transform you? What can you help me become?"

Joan with stomach cancer, for instance, found beneath her suppression of feelings was hidden a passion for excellence as a teacher and independent person. You can ask what could you do if all the energy going into illness were redirected in a more positive way. Through meditation, you find the benefits the dark side has taken from you. To see yourself as above feelings is a false sense of detachment. A truly balanced person deals with emotions not by devaluing them but by facing them, processing them and moving on.

Truly detached people are not apathetic or passive, they feel their emotions intensely and because these emotions are embraced head-on, they do not get stuck in them. They are connoisseurs of feeling, so they feel the benefits that lie below their emotions such as motivation, creativity, sexuality, productivity and love.

After you are intimate with your dark side or shadow self, then decide what you are going to change it into. What precious metal are you going to transform your base ones into? Realize that you need to create a new form of what you are going to become. Put a vision of the precious metal you are reaching to become before you. Stretch for this vision like a mountain climber throwing out your hook to where you want to be.

This attitude allows you to discover the meaning of an illness in the quietness of your mind, as objectively and honestly as possible. By reaching beyond illness, you stretch your point of view and life experience beyond the paradigm that says the past controls the future. You create a new paradigm in which the future determines the present, making decisions that cause changes in the present so that your chosen future draws you toward your destiny. You allow yourself to experiment with new ways of perceiving and experiencing life, replacing conflict with peace.

You can use the healing circles, imagery, drawing and music as tools to help you understand and feel the body language of illness. If you are denying and having difficulty being honest and objective about an illness, you can ask yourself, "What kind of thoughts, feelings and spirituality would someone with my symptoms likely have?" If you have ulcers, for instance, you might ask, "Do I resent anything or feel emotionally out of control?"

When you have an understanding of the central conflict behind an illness, you can then set a healing strategy consistent with your ideal. If you have cancer, it is likely that you need to find a genuine reason for existing, apart from pleasing others. You need to respect all your feelings more. You may also need to heal your inner child.

Judy Allen has written a book that describes the stages of her recovery from metastasized breast cancer. Her medical prognosis was that she had little chance of recovery. Instead of going through the stages of dying, Judy courageously decided to transcend her illness and use it to go through the stages of a living and higher health.

In her book, *The Stages of ~~Death and Dying~~ Life and Living,* Judy describes how instead of denying her illness, she accepted a higher path of peace for herself. The stage of denial was replaced with that of total self-acceptance of her immediate experiences and conflicts. She recognized these stresses were the result of her own previous denial of her feelings. Judy faced and expressed her desires and made the changes in her life that were necessary. She divorced her husband and got a less stressful, more satisfying job. Today, she is living a healthy, happy life.

Your healing is not complete until your conflicts are replaced by a new level of balance and peace. To stretch your experience in a more peaceful direction, make an inner decision to be honest to what is your highest truth. For Judy, this was to give up the idea that she had to live a highly stressful life as a business executive to be successful. There were other ways of feeling successful. The feminine value of just feeling good about her life became more important than a big bank account. Judy had to confront her husband with the deterioration of their marriage, forgiving both herself and him for its failure.

When you begin to transcend an illness, as Judy did, your perception of the world changes. You begin to see your world and body in a new way–not as a victim of them but as a co-creator and master of them. You begin to recreate your world and your body in a more peaceful, friendlier way. You trust yourself, both your body and your mind, to spontaneously guide you toward a more peaceful, happier and healthier life.

To make your healing task consistent with your healing ideal, you forgive and release old judgements, conflicts, fears and angers. If your ideal is to heal your resentments toward certain people, you begin recognizing you are responsible for your happiness. You, not them, need to change. You may have to go through rituals of forgiveness by expressing your feelings fully until they are released. For instance, you will know your healing from ulcers is complete when you no longer feel something is eating at you. It is your responsibility to identify this and resolve it.

Transcending Your Old Age Script

Sometimes healing involves changing beliefs and old age scripts that limit how long we think we can grow and be healthy. This is particularly true about hypertension, a condition prevalent in old age. We all have old age scripts made up of our decisions, beliefs, attitudes and choices. To discover what your old age script is, determine how you react around old people. What do you honestly believe you will become when you are old? Do you think of hypertension as a choice, or as a precondition of old age.

Some old age scripts are time bombs waiting to go off unless they are changed. To change yours, admit to yourself honestly all the things you associate with growing old. Your old age and death scripts will tell you how old you think you can live happily and how long you will live. These may need to be revised if you are to have a happy old age.

Barbara's High Blood Pressure and Old Age Script

Barbara was 68 when she came to see me to explore how she could heal her high blood pressure. Barbara said her high blood pressure began after she experienced a panic attack at the age of 65. This attack came after she saw her neighbor Ed, a man in his fifties, looking as grey as death after a heart attack. Barbara realized that Ed's illness had triggered her fear that her age now made her vulnerable to illness. Barbara's old age script was associated with helplessness, sickness, death and loss of control. She reasoned if this could happen to Ed, it could also happen to her. Later, she learned her neighbor had symptoms that made him a likely candidate for a heart attack.

Barbara was usually a courageous woman. When her old age script came into effect, this changed. What made her situation worse was her failure to make decisions to prepare for her old age, in a new community. Barbara had resistances to fulfilling her dreams because she was concerned with other people's approval.

She continued to compare her old community with her new one, rather than enjoying what the new one offered.

Healing for Barbara involved searching for and expressing her fears and then seeking for another perspective for her future. To heal herself, Barbara wrote out her old age script, burned it, and in meditation threw it into the ocean. Looking out over the ocean, she visualized the dreams she had for her old age. She received the healing image of a pilot light in the middle of her breast. To her, this represented her inner spirit which would burn away the fears. Barbara was introduced to meditation and relaxation as a way of controlling her fears. She also worked to release the beliefs she held concerning old age, which frightened and limited her.

Moving Toward Optimum Wellness

It is possible to be healthy and to be optimally well, no matter what your age. Wellness is a state of zest, gusto and enthusiasm in which you live your life with as much enjoyment and fulfillment as possible. Good health has a dynamic quality that comes from inner direction and character; it is much more than just the absence of symptoms of disease.

The Institute of Humanistic Medicine states that each individual is a synergy in which "the whole being is greater than the sum of its parts." Each of us actually has four dimensions, a physical, emotional, mental and spiritual body. Good health, by this definition, can be seen as a result of the interaction and balance among all of these bodies. Any area of growth–emotional, spiritual, physical or mental–affects all the others instantaneously.

Illness can be a breakthrough, a process of regeneration rather than degeneration. Jung noted that primitive people interpreted illness, particularly mental illness, as a transforming process. They considered illness not as a weakness of the conscious mind, but as a strong subconscious mind transforming an individual from one stage of life to another The symptoms of both physical and mental illness may indicate an individual's higher consciousness attempting to stimulate a profound self-healing process It is necessary to reduce the harmful aspects of such a transition. At the same time the ill person should be actively participating in this self-healing process. Drugs can be helpful or not; the ill person should determine whether the side effects of a drug interfere with his or her self-healing process.

Drugs often effect the quality of life of an ill individual by blunting mental or emotional responsiveness needed in healing. Healing alternatives that lack side effects, such as meditation or holistic visualization, are often good alternatives to drugs. One aspect of healing is allowing ourselves to live longer, fuller, happier lives.

Longevity

There is a negative and a positive side to living a long time. The negative side of longevity is based upon the common belief that we are just bodies. This attitude focuses only on getting rid of your symptoms or illness. Your body becomes a measure of what you are. This negative side of us measures us according to cultural standards which value youth. This attitude leads to a fear of death, because if you are your body, you lose everything at death. You control the world around you by dominating your body; by driving it and training it to be and do what you want as if it were a machine. To release the negativity of this one-dimensional attitude, you need to transcend its game and rules.

Beyond this system of thought is a higher, more positive one that sees life as a continual adventure full of fun and growth because you have created it that way. This attitude sees body, mind and spirit as working together to create what is going to be, rather than working on what used to be. This attitude sees old as beautiful, and truly appreciates the depth and richness that comes from gaining wisdom through experience. The positive side of longevity has a higher resonance that comes from keeping the excitement, enthusiasm and adventure of each moment alive.

Secrets of Longevity

The first secret of longevity is to dismantle the time bombs of your death and old age scripts and to write new ones. Death is never considered a failure in this script because it is chosen consciously when you are ready for it. The only way to effectively dismantle a death script is to transcend its narrow point of view. A new, constructive script can allow you to find meaning and beauty over and over again, in the small and large experiences of life.

The second secret of longevity is expectation. You add to your life in increments by honestly expecting to live a little longer than you originally programmed yourself to expect. If you thought you could not be happy living past 65, you allow yourself to be open to the possibility that you could live happily for another five years. When you approach 70, then allow yourself the openness to see that you could enjoy another five or six years. By allowing yourself to be open to short increments of time, you extend your life indefinitely.

Dr. Alexander Leaf took a sabbatical to visit regions of the world where people live much longer and remain more vigorous in old age than in most modern societies; Vilcambaba in Ecuador, the Hunza in West Pakistan, and the Georgian highlands in the Caucasus region of southeastern Europe. When Dr. Leaf asked the young people of Abkhazia how long they expected to live, they generally said, "To a hundred." The consensus belief in these communities was that the normal life-span is 100 years, and 80 is still a youthful age. When proposing toasts, Georgians say, "May you live 300 years," since everyone expects to reach 100.

People in the United States and other western industrial countries are programmed to live shorter lives by certain beliefs that are common in our societies and families. You may not wish to live 300 years, but expecting to live five, ten or twenty years longer can open a world of creative possibilities for you. One young man was torn between being an engineer or a musician. When he realized he could create his own longevity, he was greatly relieved. He realized he had time, to first focus on being an engineer, and later in his life he could concentrate on being a professional musician.

The third secret of longevity is to never retire from life and never stop working. You may want to retire from the company, but always have a vocation or an avocation that keeps you productive, creative and balanced. One of the factors that Leaf identified as contributing to the longevity within the communities he visited was a prolonged productive involvement in family and community affairs. Another factor was physical activity associated with this continued participation and involvement. In none of the three communities he visited was there any forced retirement. The elderly were not stuck away somewhere as is often the case in industrialized western societies.

Of those people Dr. Leaf studied, above the age of 80, more than 70% continued to be very active and more than 60% were still working. His comment was, "They die quickly once they lose useful roles in the community."

The fourth secret of longevity is to unite physical and spiritual values. This gives you a dimension beyond the senses and an openness that allows for wonder and gratitude. If you have formed a personal relationship with your higher self through quieting your mind, you can use this communion to live with more excellence and less stress.

Having regular contact with your higher consciousness reduces stress and restores your vitality, which reduces your vulnerability to illness. A time of deep meditation, especially at the beginning of the day, improves the quality of your entire day. This meditation is a quieting of the mind to listen for whatever comes to you in the silence to strengthen and inspire you.

An attitude of quiet-spiritedness is one you can carry with you throughout your daily activities. Temur Tarba, a vigorous horse-riding member of a Georgian community in the region of Abkhazia at Duripshi, in the former Soviet Union, had celebrated his hundredth birthday just before Dr. Leaf visited. He showed from his manner and attitude that he thought becoming 100 was an achievement. He smoked a good deal while talking to Dr. Leaf, but did not inhale. He devoted his mornings to picking tea and cultivating his garden. "It is best to be a youth," Temur stated, "but I have good health, feel well, have wonderful children, and I enjoy myself greatly now." He paused a moment in thought, and then added, "Every day is a gift when you are over a hundred."

The existence of these long-lived people makes us more aware that it is possible to consciously choose a longer life style. These elderly people are examples to us of intensity and involvement in life. Dr. Leaf sees in the study of these aged ones clues to preventing premature death from the three greatest killers in the United States–heart disease, cancer and stroke.

The fifth secret of longevity is to have fun and enjoy your life, by doing what you love to do. The old people in these communities are folk dancers, musicians without arthritis, and with eyes full of life and light long past one hundred years of age. What keeps these people alive and healthy, in their own words, has more to do with life satisfaction than any discipline of diet or exercise. When the research on these people is exhausted, there remains an involvement and magic to their lives that is difficult to explain. In the words of an old Abkhazian woman, "I can't explain it in scientific terms, but there just seems to be something special in the life here." The specialness of life in these communities seems to be related to the enjoyment and the freedom with which they live.

Most of these individuals maintain a strong interest in sexuality and enjoy a wide range of physical activities, including horseback riding and swimming. This vigor, enthusiasm and intensity of life are common characteristics of long-living individuals in industrialized nations as well. Research on individuals in industrialized nations who live long lives show them to be experiencing "much satisfaction" and involvement. This research indicates that an active life-style which allows for "development, change and growth to continue through the later years," despite any physical or social changes that come with old age, is an important factor in optimal health. (Pelletier, 1979)

Contrary to popular opinion, it appears that high achievers in the western world tend to live longer, healthier lives than the general population by about 30%. High achievers are usually creative people who avoid the driven Type A behavior which limits creativity and enjoyment of life. This observation is based on a twelve-year study of 6,239 men listed in the 1950-1951 edition of *Who's Who in America*. This finding shows that individuals can lead highly productive lives while maintaining good health and longevity. (Quint and Cody, 1970)

Another innovative study by physician Leslie Libow confirms the idea that good health tends to go along with purposefulness and success. Libow, of Mt. Sinai Hospital Center in New York, made an eleven-year longitudinal study of 27 "optimally healthy" men in comparison to those of 25 average men of the same age. His research found that optimally healthy men in contrast to average men had highly organized, purposeful, complex and variable daily behavior together with a lack of cigarette smoking. Being optimally healthy apparently involves choosing a lifestyle that involves both skill and challenge.

The sixth secret of longevity is to think new thoughts, feel new feelings and do new things. Many seniors make the mistake of dwelling on the past rather than creating a new life for themselves. It is important to let the past go and to refuse to stop growing. Enjoying the present and looking forward, to the new, retards the aging process. Never wait to die. Be busy with your mind, feelings and hands. Never stop growing. If you have fulfilled one destiny, create another. Find something that needs to be done in the world that is suitable to your strengths and talents, and do it. This will give you meaning and fulfillment.

For a person with an illness the future can help create a better present. It is much easier to create from the future than from the past. It is common to look to the past to justify our actions. Solutions to health problems never come from the past; they come from what the ill person can invent now and in the future. Healing is probing the future to see what exciting new state of wellness can come forth for you. Society tends to demean dreamers, but you have to dream to remain healthy. Your dreams and creative impulses are clues to ways you can live a more active, adventurous life.

198

Inner Peace is a Necessity for Health

Freedom from all of those things that cause inner conflict and imbalance; anger, fear, resentment, worry, hopelessness, doubt, confusion and anxiety, is important to continued good health. Many of the centenarians Dr. Leaf interviewed emphasized the importance of being free to do the things they enjoyed, and of maintaining a peaceful state of mind. "Now everywhere people don't live so long because they don't live a free life," commented Sonia Kvedzenia of Atara, age 109. "They worry more and don't do what they want."

The lives of the long-living people give us courage to dream our own dreams and to create alternative futures that are more healthy. We can choose those ways that are constructive, peaceful and life-nurturing, releasing those that are destructive. Behind the goal of optimal health is one of inner peace and harmony–a state of equilibrium based upon a profound inner balance. This state of consciousness is characterized by a sense of unity with all things, particularly our own bodies.

Intimacy with Our Bodies as a Key to Good Health

If you want to be healthy it is important to treat your body as your closest friend. Intimacy with this friend requires the same things you would give to any friendship. Any source of discomfort within your body needs to be removed. Success in friendship requires honesty, care and responsiveness. It is unnatural to ignore pain and discomfort in your body. It takes effort to prevent your attention from going where it wants to go. We ignore bodily signals out of fear or ignorance.

The idea that we can transcend bodily pain and illness by changing our consciousnesses is a liberating one, based upon maintaining an intimate friendship with our bodies. To accomplish this, we can overcome fears based on false medical and traditional concepts that see the body as a machine. Machines break down when their parts get old.

The human body is no machine. It has tremendous regenerative powers; no machine heals itself. No machine responds to your every emotion, thought and attitude instantaneously. No machine keeps on going even when its driver is asleep. Finally no machine is continuously replacing its own parts with new living ones. Each morning you step into a different body, because the cells of your body are constantly being replaced by new ones.

Our relationship with our bodies has much to do with whether we are ill or well. If we think of our bodies as vehicles that we can drive hard and discard, like some old Ford or Chevrolet, that is what they will become. If we instead respect them as intelligent friends that we listen to and respond to, we will live longer and healthier lives. The intelligent cells of our bodies want to be in balance and at peace. Sickness is the body's way of communicating with us, warning us to get back on the path of peace, wholeness and happiness we were always meant to be on.

Appendix

A Healing Meditation

Give yourself a moment to find a comfortable position. Take several nice deep breaths and let your eyes gently fall shut. Focus your attention on your breathing. With each in-breath, breathe in centeredness and relaxation, and with each out-breath, breathe out any tensions or fears from the day. Do not try to control your breath, just watch it as it flows in and out. As you observe the flow of your breath in and out, make your breath a little deeper to help you relax. Relax your hands, and allow your feet and legs to be uncrossed and comfortable. Adjust or shift your body if you will be more comfortable. One good way to help your body relax is to talk to your body parts to ask them gently to relax, so that is what we will do together now in preparation for meeting the image of an illness or problem and its healing.

Begin by inviting your feet to relax and let go, beginning with your smallest toe to the largest, your soles, arches and your ankles. Now invite your calves to release and let go...and all the muscles in your knees to sink and relax...the large muscles in your thighs to let go and your hips, behind, and groin to relax and let go. Now ask all the organs, muscles and nerves in your abdomen to become soft and at ease. Release any tension in your lower back. Now speak to your chest, telling it to be at ease,...telling your lungs to breathe smoothly and gently,...telling your heart to beat calmly and quietly. Speak to your upper back, telling it to relax, to release any tension stored there. Tell it to feel pleasantly warm and tingly, as

201

the relaxation improves circulation. Allow this relaxation to move to your shoulders, telling your shoulders to let go of their burdens. Let this relaxation move down to your upper arms,...your elbows,...your forearms,...wrists,...hands...and fingers. Feel your arms press more heavily on whatever they are resting on. Feel both hands and arms letting go of any fears and insecurities.

Now focus on your neck and throat. Tell your throat it has permission to express all your needs and desires. Tell your neck you are willing to be flexible and to turn in new directions, allowing it to be at ease. Let that relaxation move into your face, telling your jaw, your cheeks and your forehead to be at peace. Finally, let this relaxation sink deeply into your scalp and head. Now, rescan your whole body to see if any parts are still tense, and tell those parts to relax.

Now turn your attention to the inner screen of your mind. Imagine yourself now in a safe, beautiful and peaceful setting. This could be on a beach, in the woods, in a city park, or in your own back yard. It should be a place in which you can relax and be at peace.

This may be a place you have visited before or one you create in your imagination where you can feel peace, security and relaxation. Take a few moments to look around and notice this special, safe place. Notice what you sense there...whether there is moisture of leaves and ground...the smell of trees or the sounds of water...whether there is the feel of wind on your face...the colors of the sky or the area...notice any other sensations you have there. *(Pause.)* Now look around you until you find a comfortable place to sit or lie down; create such a spot if you need to. *(Introduce music.)* As the music begins, keep it near you, listening to it in a new way, allowing it to move in and out of your body...and to take you where you need to go.

Now direct your attention to the symptom, problem, pain or situation that is in some part of your body, mind or emotions–the thing you have come here to heal. As you focus on that sensation, allow an image to appear that represents it. Keep the music near you, and simply allow an image to emerge. *(Pause.)*

Welcome whatever image comes, whether it makes sense to you or not. Take time to observe it. What shape is it?... What color?... What size?

What is it in your life this image represents?

How do you feel about this image?

Give this image a voice, and ask it if it is trying to get your attention, or does it need your help.

When did it come into your life?

By whom is it most influenced?

How does it feel about your work?...Your relationships?... Your life-style?...Your spirituality?

What does it need from you?...Why? *(Pause.)*

In what way would it like to see your life changed?

What are healthier ways to get this same need met?

Under what circumstances would it heal or leave you?

How would it like to see you change?

Now ask for an image of the healing of this symptom or problem to appear. Simply allow it to emerge, keeping the music near you. *(Pause.)*

Focus on this image and allow it to become clearer and more vivid. Ask what it is about this image that represents healing? *(Pause.)*

Now recall the image of your illness or problem and place it beside the image of its healing. *(Pause.)* How do they seem to relate to each other?

Which is larger?...Which is more powerful? *(Pause.)*

Notice whether you can change that. *(Pause.)*

Imagine the image of healing becoming stronger, more powerful, than the image of your illness or problem...Watch that transformation...Notice how it happens...*(Pause.)*

Notice if what happens is related to anything in your life.

Can you feel or imagine any sensations as you watch this happen? Let the sensations you feel be ones of healing...Affirm to yourself that healing is happening now in your body and mind at just the right place and it continues whether you are waking...sleeping...or going about your daily activities.

Now visualize being completely healed mentally, emotionally, physically and spiritually from this problem or illness.

Take some time now to review what you have just experienced, remembering and integrating all that is important to you into your deepest mind. *(Pause.)*

When you are ready to return to the room, take a deep breath, and sigh out loud on the exhale. AAAhhh. Then open your eyes, returning to the room awake, alert, and refreshed.

(Immediately after this meditation take time to write or draw your experiences. Record any insights about your two circles–especially any feelings and their associated beliefs that relate to the meaning of your illness and its resolution. Feel the gratitude, wonder and awe in your awareness that your higher consciousness was speaking to you through the images you received. Use the drawing of your healing image as a focus of your attention. This can be placed around your home or work to remind you to heal. This image can also be used later in your regular daily healing tapes or meditations as a focus for healing.)

Appendix

Ocean Meditation for Future Wellness

Focus your attention upon your breath. Allow your breath to draw your consciousness inward. As you take your next deep inhale, breathe in relaxation and clarity of mind, and with each exhale breathe out any tensions or fears from the day. Become aware of how your body really feels upon the surface where you sit or lie, and shift your body if necessary to become as comfortable as possible. With each breath, get a sense of the rhythm of your body slowing down and moving you to a still quiet place within. The following meditation uses the imagery of a relaxing warm bath to prepare you to meet the image of your future well self.

Imagine now that there is a pool of warm liquid relaxation below your feet. With your next deep in-breath draw that liquid into your toes, the soles of your feet and your heels. This feels so good. Your feet feel like you have just stepped into a warm lovely bath. This wonderful lazy feeling spills up over your feet into your ankles and into the calves of your legs, washing away any tensions or fears. Then it fills up into your knees, thighs, pelvic area, lower abdomen, and chest area. Then it spills up over your shoulders into your arms, elbows, wrists, lower arms and hands, until both of your arms are completely filled with this relaxing liquid. This liquid of relaxation now gurgles up into your throat, chin, jaw, eyelids, and forehead, and at last fills your entire head. Notice now if you still feel any tension in any part of your body, and wash this relaxing liquid through these places. Now feel yourself being filled to the top of your head with this lovely warm relaxation, totally and completely filled, saturated and drenched, with this wonderful relaxation. You are so filled that you feel this relaxation cascading down over your shoulders, drenching and saturating your entire body.

Now that your body is completely relaxed, turn your attention to the inner screen of your mind. On that screen, imagine yourself standing alone on an ocean beach. You have come to this beach to find solitude and to imagine, feel and choose what you want for your life to become more healthy. It is the morning of a beautiful day, and you are walking on a beautiful beach alone–there is no one else in sight. You feel very safe and content to be here. Become aware of the sand under your feet as you walk along, the blueness of the water and the gentle sound of the surf at your ankles. Notice the white fluffy clouds and the seagulls flying overhead. You feel the warmth of the sun and the coolness of the sea breeze on your face. You smell the salty air.

As you walk along, you notice the little shells, chunks of wood, seaweed and the objects the sea has brought to shore. Just ahead of you on the beach is a rock that extends out into the water. You climb up on it and find a comfortable spot to lie back in the sunshine and look out at the ocean. *(Music; Debussy's* La Mer, *first movement)* As the music begins, listen to it in a new way, allowing it to touch your skin and to move in and out of your body as the waves move in and out along the shore. Ask yourself now what you need to let go of that prevents you from having the good health to desire. *(Pause.)*

Decide whether you wish to throw this into the sea. If so, see it being washed away by the waves. Look out over the ocean and feel its expansiveness and power. Feel this power and expansiveness within yourself. *(Pause.)*

Imagine now what you specifically want to be in your physical life–the health, the material things, the success or relationships you desire. *(Pause.)*

Look again out at the ocean and feel with your heart what you desire most for your spiritual life–imagine and experience that now. *(Pause.)*

You feel one with the power of the ocean. As you look out at the ocean feel and imagine what you desire in your emotional life. *(Pause.)*

Looking over the ocean again, you feel its power and beauty and your oneness with it. Now visualize what beliefs you would have if you had the mental life you truly wanted? Think these beliefs now. *(Pause.)*

You step down from the rock and draw a circle in the sand between you and the ocean. In this circle, you allow an image of the future healthy self you wish to become to appear. Talk to it about what you need to be, think or do to become more like it. *(Pause.)* Listen to what it suggests you should do or be to become more healthy.

When you are ready, step into the body of your future well self. Feel the joy, strength, wholeness and the success of that self. Feel and enjoy walking in that body. *(Pause.)* Now return to your own body.

Take some time to review and to remember all that is important to you from this experience. When you are ready, bring yourself back to the room. In a moment, open your eyes, bring your awareness back to the room, take a deep breath, stretch your arms, and wiggle your fingers. Notice whether you feel peaceful, refreshed and alert.

Freeing and Healing Your Inner Child

This meditation is for the purpose of healing and freeing the child within you. Let's begin to relax by taking a few deep breaths, and finding a comfortable quiet place to sit or lie down. Let each in-breath you take move you to the quiet place within yourself, and let each exhale release any tensions or fears from the day...breathing in centeredness and relaxation. Feel the rhythm of your body slowing down with each breath. Today we are going to use the image of a comforting blanket of energy that contains within it the energies of healing and relaxation. Now imagine there is a soft warm blanket of energy just above your feet that brings with it a soothing relaxing energy of whatever color you would like.

Now direct this blanket to come in and around your toes, tucking in your feet in just the right way. With your next inhale, breathe in this comforting energy into your toes from your little toe up to the biggest, into the soles of your feet, the arches, your heels, and moving up around your ankles, up and around your calves, tucking them in, up to your knees, around your thighs, feeling all the muscles and nerves relax. That feels so good, having your legs and feet completely relaxed, and tucked in so nicely with this warm, soft blanket.

Now see this blanket come up around your hips and groin, around your waist, tucked in perfectly. Now the blanket is brought up around your shoulders, and wrapped comfortably around you. You feel the warmth and security of this blanket of energy as it sinks into all the muscles, helping you relax so completely. Now you are all tucked in, from your neck down to your toes.

Now this same comforting healing energy shapes itself into a porous pillow for your head to sink completely into... letting go...resting on this comforting, soothing cushion. Now this magical pillow of energy moves up and around your scalp, sinking in deeply, and then moving around and back and forth along your forehead...allowing your head to be soothed. Then this comforting, relaxing energy sinks into your head, cheeks, jaw, and finally your eyelids.

Appendix

Now that your body is so comforted and well taken care of, I will count from ten down to one to allow you to reach a place of deeper relaxation. On the count of one, you will find yourself in a very particular safe place. This could be a place in your childhood where you would bring only your special friends, or it can be a meadow, or a favorite beach or park, either real or imagined. It is a place where you feel especially at ease, and safe.

10; going deeper...9; getting a sense of that particular safe place...8; beginning to get a sense of the smell of that place...7; getting a sense of what it feels like to be in your safe place...6; and what the sounds are there in that safety...5; and tasting the safety of that place...4; the special beauty that is there..3; going deeper...2; and deeper into that place...and 1; finding yourself standing in that place, finding a comfortable place to sit or lie down there. Take some time now to enjoy being in this safe place. The freedom here feels so good that you allow yourself to sing, run, dance, jump and laugh like a child with the music...*(Introduce nurturing music.)*

In your laughter you hear the laughter of a child. You turn and see your small child near as it sees it has been discovered. The child is hesitant, not knowing how you will respond and a little frightened. You reach out to it with your arms opened wide, moving toward and at last scooping up the small child into your arms. You hold your child tightly, feeling its warm breath against your cheek, its tears and your own. *(Pause.)*

You just hold the child, rocking it in your arms. In your warmth...letting it know everything will be all right. Letting it know this is only the beginning of your relationship. Tell your child now of your love and caring. How you are going to give it everything it has always wanted...that you are going to fill in the missing parts and pieces...the love the child thought it could never receive.

Now ask your child what it needs most. *(Pause.)*

Provide that now, whatever that may be. This may be a toy, a nurturing parent, a circus trip or something else entirely. *(Pause.)*

209

Now you talk to the child and and ask it what it is you have forgotten that it knows. Let the child show you or tell you what that is.

Notice the small red eyes and the shy smile that are there now. The tears have turned to smiles. Tell the child you will be available to be with it in meditation or life at a special time and place. *(Pause.)* Decide upon a special signal your child can use to get your attention when it is needed. *(Pause.)*

Give the child one last hug, making a promise to return at your appointed time. Take several deep breaths. When you are ready, open your eyes, becoming aware of the openness of your free child and the strength of your adult child joined in harmony and health.

Appendix

Meditation to Transcend Fear

Give yourself a moment to find a comfortable position, take a nice deep breath and let your eyes gently fall shut. Become aware of how your body feels resting upon the chair and, if there are any places of tension, move or shift your body to release them. Focus your attention upon your breathing and with each in-breath, breath in relaxation and clarity of mind. With each out-breath breath out any tensions or fears from the day. Just watch your breath as it flows in and out, as if your breath was breathing you. With each deep breath, get a sense of the rhythm of your body slowing down and moving you to a still quiet place within you. *(Pause.)*

You are in control of this meditation at all times and are free to accept or reject any suggestions offered. If at any time you feel afraid or wish not to continue, you may simply open your eyes and bring yourself back to the room. When you are ready, imagine yourself going to a special safe place in nature, a place of great beauty, peacefulness, and security for you. *(Pause.)* This may be a place you've visited before, either in your imagination or in outer life, or it may be a place that occurs to you right now... it doesn't really matter where you imagine yourself to be as long as it is a place of peacefulness, quiet, safety, and communion for you. *(Pause.)* Take some time to look around you and notice what you see in this place...notice what you hear ...and what you smell...and especially how good it feels to be in this place, a special place of rest, of comfort, of healing for you. *(Pause.)*

Find the spot in this special place where you feel most centered, most calm, most aware, and become comfortable in that spot... sense the connection, the centeredness, the quiet calm you feel in this spot...from here, you can observe and notice and learn. *(Pause.)* When the music begins, keep it near you and allow whatever happens to happen. Imagine that you are lying in the sunlight in your safe place. You smell the scents and the dampness of moss and grass and the scent of delicate wild flowers. You stretch out and make yourself comfortable in the warm sun,

211

looking up at the beautiful tall trees above you and at the beautiful blue sky between the trees. The warm sun is directly overhead and clouds occassionally moving by. A gentle breeze moves over your body and you feel safe and secure here, and deeply relaxed in the sunlight. *(Pause.)*

The sunlight feel so good. It seems to permeate every cell of your body. Imagine your body being transparent to sunlight, so that every cell, every organ and tissue and blood vessel, nerve and muscle in your whole body is filled with sunlight, each cell holding a little drop of sunlight, like a crystal or prism. As you inhale, imagine that the oxygen and light combine, sparkling in a rainbow of color. Imagine inhaling light and energy with every inhalation and exhaling darkness, anxiety, anger, and depression with every exhalation. Feel the calm warm energy of the sunlight coming in and darkness flowing out.

Now you feel the light from the sun over your right arm and begin to feel it penetrate the skin of your right arm from the finger tips to the shoulder. You feel it beginning to get warm and your whole body beginning to slow down and relax. Now you feel the light of the sun upon your upon your left shoulder and its warmth moves down now from your left shoulder all the way to your finger tips, so that both arms can just relax now in the light of the sun and let go.

Now you become aware of the light of the sun upon your right leg and its healing warmth moves from your toes to your hips. Perhaps you can experience the warmth of the sun penetrating every cell, muscle, nerve and the skin of your right leg. There is a comfortable warm breeze moving gently across your body. And you notice now that the light of the sun has fallen upon your left leg and from the toes to the hips you allow that leg to receive that healing light and to just relax and let go.

Now you feel the sun's warmth upon your stomach area. Your body is beginning to become peaceful and calm. Every organ, cell and nerve in your abdominal area feels filled with this healing light. Now you feel this light upon your chest and heart. You feel its light

212

and energy moving through your heart and lungs, and through your blood stream, carrying life and vibrant energy to all parts of your body. Feel it beginning to warm your chest and your heart and making it a rainbow of colors–yellow, green, blue, red, pink, orange and violet. Feel all of the colors of the rainbow within your heart area, healing and strengthening this area, and feel these colors moving out through your heart into your blood steam bringing your body healing and relaxation.

Now feel the light of the sun upon your head and feel it gently moving down your spinal column until it touches your tail bone, relaxing and moving out along every nerve that comes out from your spinal column all the way down to your tail bone. And at the same time, you feel the light of the sun upon your head, moving across your forehead, up over your head and sinking deeply within your brain, penetrating deeply, and you feel the warmth of the sun upon your face, your cheeks and jaw area. See it pentrating every cell, muscle and nerve of your cheek and jaw area, and finally you feel it across your eyelids so that your eyes feel very heavy, relaxed and yet refreshed. This feels so good, so soothing.

Into this safe place you now sense that your counselor, higher self or guide has come to lead you beyond safety to confront and transcend your fear. Sense who has come to lead you. You greet this one with a sign of affection or recognition. He or she takes you by the hand or arm and leads you beyond the safety of this place. Go searching for the place where fear resides, notice the valleys, the hills the terrain you have now entered with your guide. Is it a desert, a mountain, a forest? Feel yourself moving onward with the one who leads you there. As you walk along together, this one talks to you about your pattern or patterns of fear.

As you walk along, this one talks to you of threat. Where does your fear cluster? What is most often threatened? Does fear threaten to take away your physical needs of survival or security? Creativity, knowing, aesthetics? Are your spiritual needs threatened, the closeness, the intimacy and communication with God/Goddess/Your Soul and your higher self?

Or perhaps this one gives you images or thoughts and feelings about losing your power, your strength or talent or your true self.

Maybe it is the very essence of success that is at risk, your access to resources, your awe or wonder in your life. Or perhaps it is a loss of acceptance and love, or intimacy, a withdrawal of love, or a betrayal that is exposing your dark side. Or is it pain, destruction? What theme repeats itself? Look at the images and terrian about you. What is threatened or in jeopardy? See this. Let images and thoughts arise of these threats, this jeopardy.

Up ahead you see the place where fear resides. Hesitant, wanting to turn back–no, not this time! Together with your guide, you enter the place of fear. It may be surprising, calm and silent, with an eery stillness, yet fear is here in this pit–in this place so dark or cold or hot–fear. What is threatened? What is in jeopardy? Feel it breathing about you. What is this pit?

Is it abandonment, with its fear of rejection? Are you afraid you will be rejected or abandoned if you do not please or perform?

Is it betrayal, with a feeling that you will be humiliated if others know your ugly side?

Is it a pit of martyrdom with its punishment of others? Do you feel hopeless, helpless, unappreciated and burdened with impossible demands? How do you punish others or your higher self and soul?

Is it a demand for perfection with its blame of others?

Of defectiveness, in which you feel shame, pain or sorrow for who you are or what you have done?

Let it creep about you, let it tangle around your ankles, let it crawl up your legs and grab you by your hands.

Is this pit that of entitlement with its suffering and struggle? Or of dependency, with its expectation of devastation?

Is it a pit of alienation with its sabotage and exclusion? Let it twine about your legs, about your hips and waist and the torso of your body. Let it crawl about your neck, climbing up your face, strangely tickling, let it enter your ears and nose. You tighten your lips to keep it from your mouth. Let it engulf you and surround you.

214

Let it threat you with its suffocation, to blind and deafen you, to gag and smoother you, to silence you. Feel the fear, feel your fear, feel it. *(Pause.)* Where is the one who brought you? Why can't you feel or hear them? You feel separated; alone. Separated. *(Pause.)*

Someone is tugging at your fear. Battered about, insulted. Is that what it's all about? Horrified. Is that what it's all about? See yourself all tangled and imprisioned. See before yourself a mirror, a reflecting glass. See yourself distorted, twisted, and see beyond the glass. See a you beyond the glass (music of magic), stepping through the glass. A future you beyond your fear, a you that has already transformed this illusion. That future you pulls fear from your eyes, your mouth, your ears, pulling, tugging, cutting, thrashing to set you free, to break the paralysis. You hear the sounds of breaking away, like twigs breaking away. Reaching into your belly–wild, putrid, rancid, old fears you swallowed long ago, rotten and rancid–until all your fear is about your feet, broken. Let it be rung out of you. Let it flow out of your pores, dripping out of you about your feet. Turn your fears into juice– spilling, dripping, flowing all about your feet. The pictures into sound; the sound into silence; the silence into juice, raw, wretched, vile, the juice of emotion that once threatened and put you in jeopardy. Squeeze it out of you, tighten, the thoughts that threatened and jeopardized you now liquid, dissolving all about you.

This one has helped you be set free–the one you will be collects the vile juice and offers up your fear to the Goddess, to the maiden, the mother, the Crone. And you feel the shafts of light bouncing off your fear, radiating in all directions, the light that heals, that lifts, that transforms, that loves, everywhere healing you, healing you. You take her light and let it flow out of you into the world. It flows from you to this one who helped you and beyond the mirror into the world. Let it flow to create the specific success or successes, the images, vague or brilliant, in the world of those you love and care for. See that success, see it, hear it, touch it, taste it.

Walk out of this place that was your fear, walk step by step, one step at a time. Beyond the pit of this eroded ridge. See the success you desire, made out of your transformed fear. And there at the edge of the pit is a gift long lost in the pit of fear, at its core. Do not open, but gather, the gift. In a moment you will be back in the room awake, more alive, vibrant and aware, knowing a transformation of fear has begun. Let yourself return, take a deep breath and exhale sharply, blowing the fear out of you.

Post Script-The Scientific Basis of Body-Mind Unity

The traditional split between mind and body that has been accepted by science, is resolved by considering the body as a symbolic, informational system to which we can choose to listen and respond. This information does not belong exclusively to either mind or body, but interacts and creates both. The science of this informational feedback system gives validity and a scientific basis to the holistic theory that the physical body exists as a reflection of information that can be made conscious. Candace Pert Ph. d., who worked for many years as the Director of Biological Research at the National Institute of Health, describes the scientific basis for body-mind unity as an informational, feedback system in which the body reflects the emotional-mental attitudes of the mind-brain.

Pert has discovered that what links and holds the informational network together is the emotional limbic center of the brain which includes the hypothalamus, or the brain of the brain. In this informational network, the mind and its related emotions, link and coordinate all the major systems of the body-the immune, endocrine, nervous, and circulatory systems. In her book *Molecules of Emotion*, Pert describes the emotional limbic center of the brain as the control center or nexus between body and mind, going back and forth between the two, influencing both.

Pert describes every cell of the body as a radar receiver that gives and receives messages. There are special messenger cells called neuropeptides that are located throughout the body. These messenger and their receptor sites are found not only in the brain, but in every system of the body including the immune, endocrine, nervous, and circulatory system. These neuropeptides are described by Pert as, "the biochemical correlates of emotion." In this function, neuropeptides act as links or bridges between the physical, mental, and emotional. Every system of the body

217

communicates with every other system through neuropeptides and neuropeptide receptors. These neuropeptides are like radar discs that send out information from the brain that the cells of our bodies then react to spontaneously. Pert noticed that those places upon the body with the most receptor sites, such as the solar plexus, correspond to the major chakra areas of the body.

Since emotional expression is tied to a specific flow of peptides in the body, chronic suppression of emotions and drives disturbs the flow of this informational network. Emotions that are expressed honestly and appropriately flow through our energy systems leaving no energy blockages. When emotions are repressed, denied, or not allowed to be what they are, then the informational network of the body is blocked and cells no longer can communicate. Scientific research has associated a failure in the flow of information between cells as having a carcinogenic influence. When energy around and through an organ such as the uterus is blocked, communication between uterus cells is less and these cells then become more receptive to cancerous tumors.

The term "emotion" as Pert uses it refers to its broadest meaning which includes not only commonly considered contracting emotions such as anger, fear and grief, but also joy, contentment, and other drive states such as pleasure, pain, thirst and other drives that motivate our actions. These drives can also include the classic drives such as those for peace, love, achievement, creativity, knowledge, fun, safety, self-reliance and safety.

Pert links the body to the mind through the unconscious mind by saying, "The body is the unconscious mind." This is true because certain emotional expressions such as happiness are tied to specific flows of peptides. This flow for happiness and enthusiasm is associated with a release of the neuropeptide, norepinephrine. When people are not honest or true to their emotions, drives and needs, they in time pay a price. In time, their bodies give them the bill for their false self-esteem, self-deception, or personality drive disintegrations.

The cells in our immune systems bond with the same receptors as those that control emotional mode. Excess or inappropriate production of neuropeptides released by the immune system, brain or body, can promote cancers or latent illnesses. Pert discovered that cancer cells have neuropeptide receptors. People who are depressed secrete high levels of CRF, a corticol releasing factor which stimultes ACTH, which then stimulates the steroid corticosterone. When steroids increase in response to depression or stress and bond with available receptor sites, these sites are occupied or weakened, thus unavailable to our natural killer cells that could attack mutated and malignant cells on their way to becoming cancerous.

Healing an illness is a natural process that is within the power of all of us. Healing differs from curing because it addresses the imbalance or the hidden root conflict that either allows or creates an illness. Although there are many issues common to illnesses, there is no simple formulae for deciphering a particular illness. The ill individual knows what these messages mean, but needs to sit with their illness for a while to access the unique language of his or her body. We all have the choice to change what an experience of illness means to us emotionally, mentally, and spiritually, thus changing it physically. In this change, lies the healing of that illness. An individual with a multiple personality, for instance, can immediately heal an illness when she shifts from one personality to another. That individual, for instance, may have diabetes in one personality, but when she shifts to another personality, her diabetes will immediately heal. Researchers who study individuals with multiple personalities have learned with each personality shift, the brain wave patterns of that individual change and illnesses appear or disappear.

Since all of us contain multiple subpersonalities such as "the martyred one," "the worrier" or the "possessive lover," when we choose to change to a healthier personality, the illnesses that go with our lesser personalities can also be healed. When the body and mind are considered as a hologram, in which the body is a holographic projection of consciousness, it becomes clear that each of us is much more creative of our health than is commonly thought.

Karl Pribram, a Stanford neurosurgeon-psychologist, holds the theory that the mind and brain operate on the same principle as a photographic hologram in which all the information of the whole is contained in each of its parts. A hologram is a three dimensional photograph made with the aid of a laser. To make a hologram, the object is first bathed in the light of a laser beam. Then a second laser beam is bounced off the reflected light of the first and the resulting interfer-ence pattern, where the two laser beams commingle, is captured on film. When the film is developed and illuminated by another laser beam, a three dimensional image of the original object appears. If the hologram of an object is cut, each piece contains the entire image of that object.

Pribram observed that brain nerves branch and their messages go down the branches forming wave fronts or interference patterns similiar to those that occur in holographic photographs.

Pribram theorizes these interference waves create holograms which explain why the brain can be cut in pieces and an individual will still retain full memory. Pribram also explains how so called miraculous remissions may actually be caused by changes in consciousness which in turn effect our bodies. Techniques of visualization may work so well because holographic images in our minds are experienced ultimately as "reality," by our bodies. When conflicts are resolved on emotional, mental, and spiritual levels, physical healing can take place.

INDEX

Bibliography

Achterberg, Jeanne. *Imagery of Healing: Shamanism and Modern Medicine.* New Science Library: Shambhala Boston and London: 1985

Alexander, F.C. *Psychsomatic Medicine, Its Principles and Applications.* New York: W.W. Norton & Co., 1950

Anthonovsky, A. *Health, Stress and Coping.* San Francisco: Jossey-Bass, 1970

Arehart-Treichel. *Biotypes The Critical Link Between Personality and Your Health.* New York: Times Books, 1980

Beckman. "Lifestress and Psychological Well-Being," *Journal of Health and Social Behavior,* 1971, 12-35-45

Benson, Herbert. *The Relaxation Response.* New York: Morrow, 1975

Bulman, R.J. & C.B. Wortman "Attribution of blame and coping in the 'real world:'Severe accident victims react to their lot," *Journal of Personality and Social Psychology.* 1977 (35) 351-363.

Cobb, S. & R.M. Rose. "Hypertension, peptic ulcer and diabetes in air traffic controllers," *Journal of the American Medical Association* (224) 489-493

Cousins, Norman. *Anatomy of an Illness.* New York: Bantam, 1981

Cousins, Norman. *The Healing Heart: Antidotes to Panic and Helplessness.* G.K. Hall, 1983

Dudley, Donald and Elton Welke. *How to Survive Being Alive: Stress Points and Your Health.* Garden City, NewYork: 1977

Farquhar, John, M.D. *The American Way of Life Need Not Be Hazardous to Your Health.* New York: W.W. Norton & Co., 1978

Frazier, Claude. *Psychosomatic Aspects of Allergy.* Van Nostrand Reinhold Co., 1977

Friedman, Meyer and Diane Ulmer. *Treating Type-A Behavior and Your Heart.* New York: Alfred A. Knopf, 1984

226

Gauser, Bernard . "Why Do Some People Survive AIDS?" *Parade Magazine,* in The Spokesman-Review–Spokane Chronicle, September 18, 1988, 4-7.

Gordon, James, Dennis Jaffee and David Bressler. *Mind, Body and Health: Toward an Integral Medium.* New York: Human Sciences Press, Inc., 1984.

Grace, William and David Graham. "The specificity of the relation bewteen attitudes and disease," *Psychosomatic Medicine,* vol. 14. 1952, 243-251.

Graham, Stern and G. Hinoker. "Experimental investigation of the Specificity of Attitude hypothesis in psychomatic disease," *Psychomatic Medicine,* vol.20. 1958, 446-457.

Graham, D., R.M. Lundy, L.S. Benjamin, J.D. Kabler, W.C. Lewis, N.O. Kunish and F.K. Graham. "Specific attitudes in initial interviews with patients having different 'psychosomatic' disease," *Psychosomatic Medicine,* vol. 24. 1962, 257.

Graham, D.T. "Health, disease and the mind-body problem: linguistic parallelism," *Psychosomatic Medicine,* vol. 29. 1967, 52-71.

Hay, Louise L. *You Can Heal Your Life.* New York: Coleman Publishing Co., 1984

Hutschnecher, Arnold, A.M.D. *The Will to Live.* New York: Cornerstone Library, 1982

Jaffe, Dennis T. *Healing From Within.* New York: Alfred A. Knopf, Inc., 1980

Jampolsky, Gerald, M.D. *Teach Only Love.* New York: Bantam Books, 1983

Johnson, J.H. and I.G. Saranson. "Life stress, depression and anxiety: Internal-external control as a moderator variable," *Journal of Psychomatic Research,* 1978, (22), 205-208.

Jolly, Dr. Richard T. *The Color Atlas of Human Anatomy.* New York: Beekman House, 1980.

Kapic, Wynn and Lawrence M. Elson. *The Anatomy Coloring Book.* New York: Harper and Row Publishers, Inc., 1977

Kaufman, Barry Neil. *A Sense of Warning.* Delacorte Press 1983.

Kobasa, S.C. "Stressful life events, personality and health: an inquiry into hardiness," *Journal of Personality and Social Psychology.* 1979, (37), 1-11.

Kobasa, S.C., S.R. Maddi and S. Kahn. "Hardiness and health: a prospective study," *Journal of Personality and Social Psychology.* 1979, (42), 168-177.

Kobasa, S.C. and M.C. Puccetti. "Personality and social resources in stress resistance," *Journal of Personality and Social Psychology.* 1983, (45).

Lazaris. Lazaris Interview Book I. Concept: Synergy Publishing, 1988.

Lazaris. The Chakras (audiotape).

Lazaris. The Healing: The Nature of Health, Tapes I and II (audio).

Lazaris. *The Unseen Friends.*

LeShan, Lawrence. *The Mechanic and the Gardener.* New York: Holt, Reinhart and Winston, 1982.

LeShan, Lawrence. The *Medium, the Mystic and the Physicist.* New York, Ballantine Books, 1975.

LeShan, Lawrence. *You Can Fight For Your Life.* New York, Jove Publications, 1977.

Leaf, A. "Every day is a gift when you are over 100," *National Geographic.* 1973, 143 (1), 93-118.

Lewis, R. *The Way of Silence: The Prose and Poetry of Basho.* New York, Dial Press, 1970.

Libow, L.S. "Interaction of medical, biological and behavioral factors on aging, adaption and survival: an 11-year longitudinal study," *Geriatrics.* 1974, 29 (1), 75-88.

Moss, Gordan. *Illness, Immunity and Social Interaction.* New York, Wiley, 1973

Pelletier, Kenneth. *Holistic Medicine from Stress to Optimum Health.* Delacorte Press, Seymour Lawrence, 1979.

Pelletier, Kenneth. *Mind as Healer, Mind as Slayer.* New York: Dell Publishing Co., 1977.

Porter, Garret and Patricia Norris. *Why Me?* Stillpoint Publishing

Co., 1985.

Price, V.A. *Type-A Behavior Pattern: A Model for Research and Practice.* New York, Academic Press, 1982.

Rossman, Martin. *Healing Yourself.* Walker & Co., 1987.

Schmale, A.H. and H. Iker. "Hopelessness as a predicator of cervical cancer," *Social Science and Medicine.* 1971, (5), 95-100.

Seligman, M E. *Helplessness.* San Francisco, Freeman, 1975.

Selye, Hans. "The secret of coping with stress," interview in *U.S. News and World Report.* March 21, 1977, 51-53.

Selye, Hans. *The Stress of Life.* New York, McGraw-Hill, 1956.

Siegel, Bernie. *Love, Medicine and Miracles.* New York: Harper & Row Publishers, 1986.

Simonton, O. Carl, Stephanie Matthew-Simonton and James Creighton. *Getting Well Again.* New York: J.P. Tarcher, Bantam. 1978.

Sontag, Susan. *Illness as a Metaphor.* New York: Farrar, Straus & Giroux, 1977.

Temoshok, Lydia, Craig Van Dyke and Leonard Zegans. *Emotions in Health and Illness.* New York: Grune & Stratton, 1983.

Temoshok, Lydia and Henry Dreher. *The Type-C Connection: The Behavioral Links to Cancer and Your Health.* New York: Random House, 1992.

Wolf, Stewart and Helen Goodel. *Harold G. Wolff's Stress Disease,* revised and edited. Springfield, Illinois: Charles C. Thomas, 1968.